Taran Mullh?

It's another Quality Book from CGP

This book is for anyone doing AQA Modular GCSE Mathematics
at Higher Level.

Whatever subject you're doing it's the same
old story — there are lots of facts and you've just got
to learn them. KS4 Maths is no different.

Happily this CGP book gives you all that important
information as clearly and concisely as possible.

It's also got some daft bits in to try and make the whole
experience at least vaguely entertaining for you.

What CGP is all about

Our sole aim here at CGP is to produce the highest quality books
— carefully written, immaculately presented and dangerously
close to being funny.

Then we work our socks off to get them out to you
— at the cheapest possible prices.

Contents

Published by Coordination Group Publications Ltd.

Written by Richard Parsons

Updated by Alison Chisholm, Sharon Keeley, Simon Little, Mark Moody, Alison Palin,
Bob Summers, Claire Thompson, Mark Turner, Sharon Watson

ISBN 1 84146 094 X

Groovy website: www.cgpbooks.co.uk

With thanks to Ann Francis, Sam Norman and Glenn Rogers for the proofreading.

Printed by Elanders Hindson, Newcastle upon Tyne.

Text, design, layout and original illustrations © Richard Parsons 2004

Mean, Median, Mode and Range

If you don't manage to _learn these 4 basic definitions_ then you'll be passing up on some of the easiest marks in the whole Exam. It can't be _that_ difficult can it?

1) **_MODE_** = **_MOST_** common

2) **_MEDIAN_** = **_MIDDLE_** value

3) **_MEAN_** = **_TOTAL of items_** ÷ **_NUMBER of items_**

4) **_RANGE_** = **_How far from the smallest to the biggest_**

THE GOLDEN RULE

Mean, median and mode should be _easy marks_ but even people who've gone to the incredible extent of learning them still manage to lose marks in the Exam because they don't do _this one vital step_:

Always REARRANGE the data in ASCENDING ORDER

(and check you have the same number of entries!)

Example   _"Find the mean, median, mode and range of these numbers:"_

2, 5, 3, 2, 6, –4, 0, 9, –3, 1, 6, 3, –2, 3   (14)

1) FIRST... rearrange them: –4, –3, –2, 0, 1, 2, 2, 3, 3, 3, 5, 6, 6, 9   (14)✓

2) MEAN = $\frac{\text{total}}{\text{number}}$ = $\dfrac{-4-3-2+0+1+2+2+3+3+3+5+6+6+9}{14}$

= 31 ÷ 14 = <u>2.21</u>

3) MEDIAN = _the middle value_ (only when they are _arranged in order of size_, that is!).

When there are two middle numbers as in this case, then the median is **HALFWAY BETWEEN THE TWO MIDDLE NUMBERS**

> –4, –3, –2, 0, 1, 2, 2, 3, 3, 3, 5, 6, 6, 9
> ← seven numbers this side ↑ seven numbers this side →
> Median = <u>2.5</u>

4) MODE = _most_ common value, which is simply <u>3</u>. (_Or you can say "The modal value is 3"._)

5) RANGE = distance from lowest to highest value, i.e. from –4 up to 9, = <u>13</u>

REMEMBER: <u>Mo</u>de = <u>mo</u>st (emphasise the 'o' in each when you say them)
<u>Med</u>ian = <u>mid</u> (emphasise the m*d in each when you say them)
<u>Mean</u> is just the <u>average</u>, but it's <u>mean</u> 'cos you have to work it out.

The Acid Test: LEARN The Four Definitions and THE GOLDEN RULE...

...then turn this page over and _write them down from memory_. Then apply all that you have _learnt_ to this set of data: 1, 3, 14, –5, 6, –12, 18, 7, 23, 10, –5, –14, 0, 25, 8.

Probability

Combined Probability — two or more events

This is where most people start getting into trouble, and d'you know why?
I'll tell you — it's because they don't know these three simple rules:

Three Simple Rules:

1) <u>Always break down</u> a complicated-looking probability question into <u>A SEQUENCE</u> of <u>SEPARATE SINGLE EVENTS</u>.

2) <u>Find the probability of EACH</u> of these <u>SEPARATE SINGLE EVENTS</u>.

3) <u>Apply the AND/OR rule</u>:

1) *The AND Rule:*

$$P(A \text{ and } B) = P(A) \times P(B)$$

Which means: The probability of Event A AND Event B BOTH happening is equal to the two separate probabilities MULTIPLIED together.

(Strictly speaking, the two events have to be <u>INDEPENDENT</u>. All that means is that one event happening does not in any way affect the probability of the other one from happening. Contrast this with mutually exclusive below.)

2) *The OR Rule:*

$$P(A \text{ or } B) = P(A) + P(B)$$

Which means: The probability of <u>EITHER Event A OR Event B</u> happening is equal to the two separate probabilities <u>ADDED together</u>.

(Strictly speaking, the two events have to be <u>MUTUALLY EXCLUSIVE</u>, which means that if one event happens, the other one can't happen. Pretty much the opposite of independent events (see above).)

The way to remember this is that it's the <u>wrong way round</u> — i.e. you'd want the AND to go with the + but it doesn't: It's "<u>AND with x</u>" and "<u>OR with +</u>".

Example

"Find the probability of picking two kings from a pack of cards (assuming you don't replace the first card picked)."

<u>ANSWER:</u>

1) <u>SPLIT</u> this into TWO SEPARATE EVENTS

— i.e. picking the <u>first king</u> *and then* <u>picking the second king</u>.

2) *Find the SEPARATE probabilities* of these *two separate events*:

P (first king) = $\frac{4}{52}$ P (second king) = $\frac{3}{51}$ (note the change from 52 to 51 and 4 to 3)

3) *Apply the AND/OR Rule:* BOTH events must happen, so it's the AND rule:

so <u>multiply</u> the two separate probabilities: $\frac{4}{52} \times \frac{3}{51} = \frac{1}{221}$

The Acid Test: LEARN the <u>Three Simple Rules</u> for <u>multiple events</u>, and <u>the AND/OR Rule</u>.

1) Now turn over and write these rules down <u>from memory</u>. Then apply them to this:

2) Find the probability of picking 2 queens plus the ace of spades from a pack of cards.

Probability

THE SINGLE MOST IMPORTANT FACT you can learn about probability is this:

Every Probability Question should be done using a Tree Diagram.

And _once you register that sweet simple truth_ the whole torrid subject suddenly begins to settle into sublime serenity. And why? — because once you've _thoroughly learnt_ the handful of details below on how to do tree diagrams you can tackle EVERY probability question they can throw at you using the EXACT SAME METHOD every time! Sounds too good? Well it's true, so believe it!

There are TWO THINGS YOU MUST DO however to attain this happy state:

1) Thoroughly LEARN all these details on TREE DIAGRAMS and practise applying them.

2) Make it a HABIT to START DRAWING A TREE DIAGRAM (as small and scruffy as you like) the moment you see any probability question.

General Tree Diagram

All Tree Diagrams have a lot of details in common. It's pretty essential that you know these details, because without them, you won't be able to use tree diagrams to do the questions in the Exam. _You need to know this diagram inside out:_

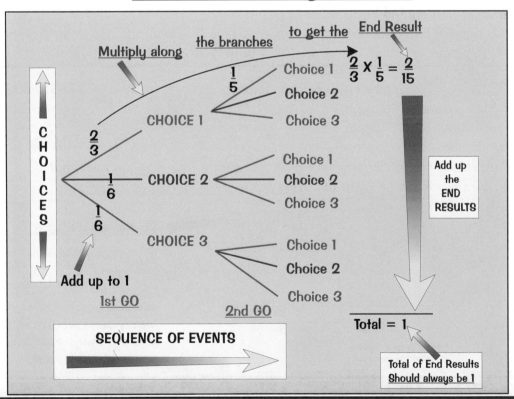

1) Always _multiply_ the numbers _along the branches_ to get the END RESULTS.

2) The numbers _on any set of branches which all meet at a point_ must always ADD UP TO 1.

3) Check that your diagram is correct by _making sure the End Results_ ADD UP TO 1.

4) To answer any question, simply ADD up the RELEVANT END RESULTS.

AQA MODULAR MATHS — MODULE ONE

Probability

Four Extra Details for the Tree Diagram method:

1) Always break up the question INTO A SEQUENCE OF SEPARATE EVENTS.

E.g. "3 coins are tossed together" — just split it into 3 separate events. *You need this sequence of events* to be able to draw any sort of tree diagram.

2) DON'T FEEL you have to draw COMPLETE tree diagrams.

Learn to adapt them to what is required. E.g. "What is the chance of throwing a dice 3 times and getting 2 sixes followed by an even number?" This diagram is all you need to get the answer $\frac{1}{6} \times \frac{1}{6} \times \frac{1}{2} = \frac{1}{72}$

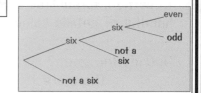

3) WATCH OUT for CONDITIONAL PROBABILITIES.

...where the fraction on each branch depends on what happened *on the previous branch*, e.g. bags of sweets, packs of cards, etc., where the *bottom* number of the fractions *also* changes as items are removed. E.g. $\frac{11}{25}$ then $\frac{10}{24}$, etc.

4) With "AT LEAST" questions, it's always (1 – Prob of "the other outcome").

For example, *"Find the probability of having AT LEAST one girl in 4 kids"*
There are in fact *15 different ways* of having "AT LEAST one girl in 4 kids" which would take a long time to work out, even with a tree diagram.
The clever trick you should know is this:
The prob of *"AT LEAST something or other"* is just (1 – prob of "the other outcome") which in this case is   (1 – prob of "all 4 boys") = (1 – 1/16) = 15/16.

Example

"Herbert and his two chums, along with five of Herbert's doting aunties, have to squeeze onto the back seat of his father's Bentley, en route to Royal Ascot. Given that Herbert does not sit at either end, and that the seating order is otherwise random, find the probability of Herbert having his best chums either side of him."

The untrained probabilist wouldn't think of using a tree diagram here, but see how easy it is when you do. *This is the tree diagram you'd draw:*

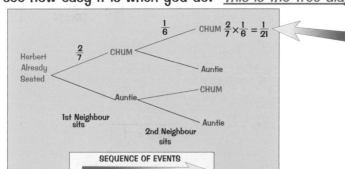

So the answer is 1/21.

Of course you'd have to do a bit of thinking to decide to place Herbert first and then have the two events as each of his "neighbours" are placed beside him, but that sort of trick is pretty standard really.

The Acid Test:

LEARN ALL OF PAGE 3 AND 4. Then <u>turn over and write down</u> all the key points and the example too.

1) As it turned out the Bentley could only seat 6 people across so the last two in had to sit on other people's laps. Find the probability that Herbert had his best chums either side and no doting Auntie on his lap.

2) Find TEN probability questions, and practise tackling them with TREE DIAGRAMS.

Relative Frequency

This isn't the number of times your granny comes to visit.
It's a way of working out probabilities.

Fair or Biased?

The probability of rolling a three on a dice is $\frac{1}{6}$ — you know that each
of the 6 numbers on a dice is <u>equally likely</u> to be rolled, and there's <u>only 1 three</u>.
BUT this only works if it's a <u>fair dice</u>. If the dice is a bit <u>wonky</u> (the technical term is "biased")
then each number <u>won't</u> have an equal chance of being rolled. That's where <u>Relative</u>
<u>Frequency</u> comes in — you can use it to work out probabilities when things might be wonky.

Do the Experiment *Again* and *Again* and *Again* and *Again*

You need to do an experiment <u>over and over again</u> and then do a quick calculation.
(Remember, an experiment could just mean rolling a dice.)
Usually the results of these experiments will be written in a <u>table</u>.

The Formula for Relative Frequency

$$\text{Probability of something happening} = \frac{\text{Number of times it has happened}}{\text{Number of times you tried}}$$

You can work out the relative frequency as a <u>fraction</u>, but usually
<u>decimals</u> are best for comparing the relative frequencies.

The important thing to remember is:

**The more times you do the experiment,
the more accurate the probability will be.**

Example:

So, back to the wonky dice. <u>What is the probability of rolling a three?</u>

Number of Times the dice was rolled	10	20	50	100
Number of threes rolled	2	5	11	23
Relative frequency	$\frac{2}{10}=0.2$	$\frac{5}{20}=0.25$	$\frac{11}{50}=0.22$	$\frac{23}{100}=0.23$

So, what's the probability? We've got <u>4 possible answers</u>, but the best is the one
worked out using the <u>highest number of dice rolls</u>.
This makes the probability of rolling a three on this dice 0.23.

And since for a fair, unbiased dice, the probability of rolling a three is $\frac{1}{6}$ (about 0.17),
then our dice <u>is biased</u>.

Frequency Tables

Frequency Tables can either be done in _rows_ or in _columns_ of numbers, and they can be quite confusing — <u>but not if you learn these Eight key points:</u>

Eight Key Points

1) <u>ALL FREQUENCY TABLES ARE THE SAME</u>.

2) The word <u>FREQUENCY</u> just means <u>HOW MANY</u>, so a frequency table is nothing more than a "<u>How many in each group</u>" table.

3) The <u>FIRST ROW</u> (or column) just gives the <u>GROUP LABELS</u>.

4) The <u>SECOND ROW</u> (or column) gives the <u>ACTUAL DATA</u>.

5) You have to <u>WORK OUT A THIRD ROW</u> (or column) <u>yourself</u>.   *Hold on, we'll get to this on P.7*

6) The <u>MEAN</u> is always found using: | 3rd Row total ÷ 2nd Row Total |

7) The <u>MEDIAN</u> is found from the <u>MIDDLE VALUE</u> in the 2nd row.

8) The <u>RANGE</u> is found from <u>the extremes of the first row</u>.

Example

Here is a typical frequency table shown in both <u>ROW FORM</u> and <u>COLUMN FORM</u>:

No. of Sisters	Frequency
0	7
1	15
2	12
3	8
4	3
5	1
6	0

No. of Sisters	0	1	2	3	4	5	6
Frequency	7	15	12	8	3	1	0

 Column Form

 Row form

There's no real difference between these two forms and you could get either one in your Exam. Whichever you get, make sure you remember these <u>THREE IMPORTANT FACTS</u>:

1) <u>THE 1ST ROW</u> (or column) gives us the <u>GROUP LABELS</u> for <u>the different categories</u>: i.e. "no sisters", "one sister", "two sisters", etc.

2) <u>THE 2ND ROW</u> (or column) <u>is the ACTUAL DATA</u> and tells us <u>HOW MANY (people) THERE ARE</u> in each category i.e. 7 people had "<u>no sisters</u>", 15 people had "<u>one sister</u>", etc.

3) <u>BUT YOU SHOULD SEE THE TABLE AS _UNFINISHED_</u>, because it still needs <u>A THIRD ROW</u> (or column) and <u>TWO TOTALS</u> for the <u>2nd and 3rd rows</u>, as shown on the next page:

Frequency Tables

This is what the two types of table look like when they're completed:

No. of sisters	0	1	2	3	4	5	6	totals	
Frequency	7	15	12	8	3	1	0	46	(People asked)
No. x Frequency	0	15	24	24	12	5	0	80	(Sisters)

No. of Sisters	Frequency	No. x Frequency
0	7	0
1	15	15
2	12	24
3	8	24
4	3	12
5	1	5
6	0	0
TOTALS	46	80

(People asked)   (Sisters)

"Where does the third row come from?" ...I hear you cry!

THE THIRD ROW (or column) is ALWAYS obtained by MULTIPLYING the numbers FROM THE FIRST 2 ROWS (or columns).

THIRD ROW = 1ST ROW × 2ND ROW

Once the table is complete, you can easily find the MEAN, MEDIAN, MODE AND RANGE (see P.1) which is what they usually demand in the Exam:

Mean, Median, Mode and Range:

This is easy enough *if you learn it*. If you don't, you'll drown in a sea of numbers.

1) MEAN = $\dfrac{\text{3rd Row Total}}{\text{2nd Row Total}}$ = $\dfrac{80}{46}$ = 1.74 (Sisters per person)

2) MEDIAN: — imagine the original data *SET OUT IN ASCENDING ORDER*:

0000000 111111111111111 222222222222 33333333 444 5
                                    ↑

and the median is just the middle, which is here between the 23rd and 24th digits. So for this data THE MEDIAN IS 2.

(Of course, when you get slick at this you can easily find the position of the middle value straight from the table.)

3) The MODE is *very easy* – it's just THE GROUP WITH THE MOST ENTRIES: i.e. 1

4) The RANGE is 5 – 0 = 5   The first row tells us there are people with anything from "no sisters" right up to "five sisters" (but not 6 sisters).   (Always give it as a single number.)

The Acid Test:

LEARN the 8 RULES for Frequency Tables, then turn over and WRITE THEM DOWN to see what you know.

Using the methods you have just learned and this frequency table, find the MEAN, MEDIAN, MODE and RANGE of the no. of phones that people have.

No. of Phones	0	1	2	3	4	5	6
Frequency	1	25	53	34	22	5	1

Grouped Frequency Tables

These are a bit trickier than simple frequency tables, but they can still look deceptively simple, like this one which shows the distribution of weights of a bunch of 60 school kids.

Weight (kg)	31 — 40	41 — 50	51 — 60	61 — 70	71 — 80
Frequency	8	16	18	12	6

Class Boundaries and Mid-Interval Values

These are the two little jokers that make Grouped Frequency tables so tricky.

1) THE CLASS BOUNDARIES are the precise values where you'd pass from one group into the next. For the above table the class boundaries would be at 40.5, 50.5, 60.5, etc. It's not difficult to work out what the class boundaries will be, just so long as you're clued up about it — they're nearly always 'something.5' anyway, for obvious reasons.

You'll sometimes be given the classes as inequalities.
E.g. the class 41-50 might be written as $40.5 \leq w < 50.5$.

2) THE MID-INTERVAL VALUES are pretty self-explanatory really and usually end up being "something.5" as well. Mind you a bit of care is needed to make sure you get the exact middle!

'Estimating' The Mean using Mid-Interval Values

Just like with ordinary frequency tables you have to *add extra rows and find totals* to be able to work anything out. Also notice you can only 'estimate' the mean from grouped data tables — you can't find it exactly unless you know all the original values.

1) Add a 3rd row and enter MID-INTERVAL VALUES for each group.
2) Add a 4th row and multiply FREQUENCY × MID-INTERVAL VALUE for each group.

Weight (kg)	31 — 40	41 — 50	51 — 60	61 — 70	71 — 80	TOTALS
Frequency	8	16	18	12	6	60
Mid-Interval Value	35.5	45.5	55.5	65.5	75.5	—
Frequency × Mid-Interval Value	284	728	999	786	453	3250

1) ESTIMATING THE MEAN is then the usual thing of DIVIDING THE TOTALS:

$$\text{Mean} = \frac{\text{Overall Total (Final Row)}}{\text{Frequency Total (2nd Row)}} = \frac{3250}{60} = 54.2$$

2) THE MODE is still nice 'n' easy: the modal group is 51 — 60kg

3) THE MEDIAN can't be found exactly but you can at least say which group it's in. If all the data were put in order, the 30th/31st entries would be in the 51 — 60kg group.

The Acid Test:

LEARN all the details on this page, then turn over and write down everything you've learned. Good clean fun.

1) Estimate the mean for this table:
2) Also state the modal group and the approximate value of the median.

Length(cm)	15.5 —	16.5 —	17.5 —	18.5 — 19.5
Frequency	12	18	23	8

Cumulative Frequency

FOUR KEY POINTS

1) CUMULATIVE FREQUENCY just means <u>ADDING IT UP AS YOU GO ALONG</u>.

2) You have to <u>ADD A THIRD ROW</u> to the table — the <u>RUNNING TOTAL</u> of the 2nd row.

3) <u>When plotting the graph</u>, always plot points <u>using the HIGHEST VALUE in each group</u> (of row 1) with the value from <u>row 3</u>, i.e. plot 13 at <u>160.5</u>, etc. (see below).

4) CUMULATIVE FREQUENCY is always plotted <u>up the side</u> of a graph, not across.

Example

Height (cm)	141 – 150	151 – 160	161 – 170	171 – 180	181 – 190	191 – 200	201 – 210
Frequency	4	9	20	33	36	15	3
Cumulative Frequency	4 (AT 150.5)	13 (AT 160.5)	33 (AT 170.5)	66 (AT 180.5)	102 (AT 190.5)	117 (AT 200.5)	120 (AT 210.5)

The graph is plotted from these pairs: (150.5,4) (160.5,13) (170.5,33) (180.5,66) etc.

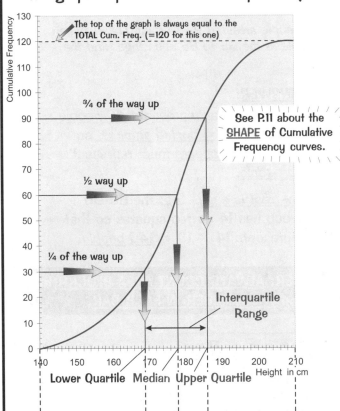

The top of the graph is always equal to the TOTAL Cum. Freq. (=120 for this one)

¾ of the way up

½ way up

¼ of the way up

See P.11 about the <u>SHAPE</u> of Cumulative Frequency curves.

Interquartile Range

Lower Quartile   Median   Upper Quartile

For a cumulative frequency curve there are **THREE VITAL STATISTICS** which you need to know how to find:

1) **MEDIAN**
Exactly halfway UP, then across, then down and *read off the bottom scale*.

2) **LOWER AND UPPER QUARTILES**
Exactly ¼ and ¾ UP the side, then across, then down and *read off the bottom scale*.

3) **THE INTERQUARTILE RANGE**
The distance *on the bottom scale* between the lower and upper quartiles.

So from the cumulative frequency curve for this data, we get these results:
MEDIAN = <u>178 cm</u>
LOWER QUARTILE = <u>169 cm</u>
UPPER QUARTILE = <u>186 cm</u>
INTERQUARTILE RANGE = <u>17 cm</u> (186 — 169)

A Box Plot shows the Interquartile Range as a Box

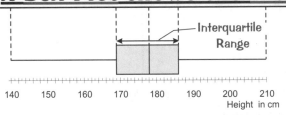

Interquartile Range

TO CREATE YOUR VERY OWN BOX PLOT:

1) *Draw the scale* along the bottom.
2) *Draw a box* the length of the *interquartile range*.
3) *Draw a line* down the box to show the *median*.
4) *Draw "whiskers"* up to the *maximum and minimum*.

(They're sometimes called "box and whisker diagrams".)

The Acid Test:

LEARN THIS PAGE, then <u>cover it up</u> and do these:

1) *Complete* this cumulative frequency table:
2) *Draw the graph*. Find the *3 Vital Statistics*.
3) Draw the box plot under the graph.

Weight (kg)	41 – 45	46 – 50	51 – 55	56 – 60	61 – 65	66 – 70	71 – 75
Frequency	2	7	17	25	19	8	2

Histograms and Frequency Density

Histograms

A histogram is like a bar chart with different width bars — the AREA, NOT the HEIGHT, of each bar gives the FREQUENCY.

This changes them from nice easy-to-understand diagrams into seemingly incomprehensible monsters, and yes, you've guessed it, that makes them a _firm favourite_ with the Examiners.

In fact things aren't half as bad as that — but only if you LEARN THE THREE RULES:

> 1) It's <u>not</u> the height, but the <u>AREA of each bar that matters</u>.
> 2) <u>Use the snip of information they give you</u> to find
>   <u>HOW MUCH IS REPRESENTED BY EACH AREA BLOCK</u>.
> 3) <u>Divide all the bars into THE SAME SIZED AREA BLOCKS</u>
>   and so work out the number for each bar (using AREAS).

EXAMPLE:

The histogram below represents the age distribution of people arrested for slurping boiled sweets in public places in 1995. Given that there were 40 people in the 55 to 65 age range, find the number of people arrested in all the other age ranges.

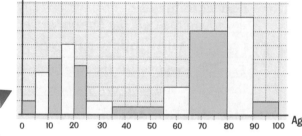

Frequency Density

The vertical axis is always called frequency density...

ANSWER:

The 55-65 bar represents _40 people_ and contains _4 dotted squares_, so _each dotted square_ must represent _10 people_.

The rest is easy. E.g. the 80-90 group has 14 dotted squares so that represents 14 × 10 = _140 people_.

> REMEMBER: <u>ALWAYS COUNT AREA BLOCKS</u> to find <u>THE NUMBER IN EACH BAR</u>.

Frequency Density is the Height of a Bar

You don't need to worry too much about this. It says in the syllabus that you need to understand frequency density, so here it is. Learn the formula and you'll be fine.

> **FREQUENCY DENSITY = FREQUENCY ÷ CLASS WIDTH**
>
> _Frequency density = the height of a bar._
> _Frequency = the area of a bar_
> _Class width = the width of the bar along the x-axis._

EXAMPLE: For the 55-65 bar: frequency = 40 people, class width = 10 years
    Frequency density = frequency ÷ class width
So: Frequency density = 40 ÷ 10 = 4 — _the height of the bar._

The Acid Test:
LEARN the <u>THREE RULES for Histograms</u> and the formula for <u>frequency density</u>. <u>Turn over and write it all down</u>.

1) Find the number of people arrested in each of the age ranges for the boiled sweet histogram above.
2) If the frequency is 25 and the class width is 5, what is the frequency density?

Correlation, Dispersion and Spread

Scatter Graphs — correlation and the line of best fit

A scatter graph tells you how closely two things are related — the fancy word for this is _CORRELATION_. _Good correlation_ means the two things are _closely related_ to each other. _Poor correlation_ means there is _very little relationship_. The _LINE OF BEST FIT_ goes roughly _through the middle of the scatter of points_. (It doesn't have to go through any of the points exactly, but it can.) If the line slopes _up_ it's _positive correlation_, if it slopes _down_ it's _negative correlation_. _No correlation_ means there's no _linear relationship_.

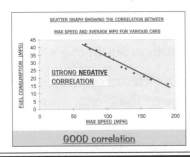

GOOD correlation

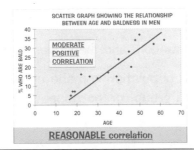

REASONABLE correlation

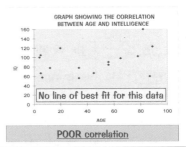

POOR correlation

Shapes of Histograms and "Spread"

You can easily estimate the mean from the shape of a histogram — it's more or less **IN THE MIDDLE**.

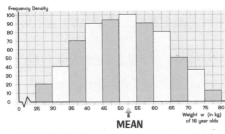

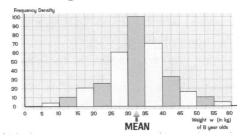

You must _LEARN the significance of the shapes_ of these two histograms:

1) The first shows _high dispersion_ (i.e. a _large spread_ of results away from the mean).
   (i.e. the weights of a sample of 16 year olds will cover a very wide range)

2) The second shows a _"tighter"_ distribution of results where most values are within a _narrow range_ either side of the mean.
   (i.e the weights of a sample of 8 year olds will show _very little_ variation)

Cumulative Freq. Curves and "Spread"

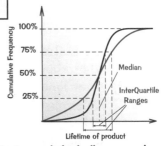

The shape of a _CUMULATIVE FREQUENCY CURVE_ also tells us _how spread out_ the data values are.

The _blue_ line shows a _very tight distribution_ around the MEDIAN and this also means the _interquartile range is small_ as shown.

The _red_ line shows a more _widely spread_ set of data and therefore a _larger interquartile range_.

The 'tighter' distribution represents very CONSISTENT results, e.g. _lifetimes of batteries or light bulbs_ very close to the median indicate a _better product_, compared to the distribution of a less consistent product where the lifetimes show a _wide variation_ (with the same median). They often ask about this _"shape significance"_ in Exams.

The Acid Test:
LEARN THIS PAGE. Then _turn over_ and _write down all the important details_ from memory.

1) Draw two contrasting histograms showing speeds of cyclists and motorists.
2) Sketch two cumulative frequency curves for heights of 5 yr olds and 13 yr olds.

Sampling Methods

This is all about doing surveys of "populations" (not necessarily people) to find things out about them. Things start getting awkward when it's not possible to test the whole "population", usually because there's just too many.

In that case you have to take a <u>SAMPLE</u>, which means <u>you somehow have to select a limited number of individuals so that they properly represent the whole "population"</u>.

There are <u>THREE DIFFERENT TYPES OF SAMPLING</u> which you should know about:

<u>RANDOM</u> — this is where you just select individuals "at random". In practice it can be surprisingly difficult to make the selection truly random.

<u>SYSTEMATIC</u> — E.g. select one at random and then select every 10th or 100th one after that.

<u>STRATIFIED</u> — this is used when a population is made up of groups (or categories). A <u>random</u> sample is chosen in each group, <u>proportional</u> to the size of the group.

E.g. In a school there are 400 girls and 600 boys — 1000 students.
For a total sample of 50 you need to <u>randomly</u> choose 20 girls and 30 boys.

Spotting Problems with Sampling Methods

In practice, the most important thing you should be able to do is to spot problems with sampling techniques, which means "<u>look for ways that the sample might not be a true reflection of the population as a whole</u>".

One mildly amusing way to practise is to think up examples of <u>bad sampling techniques</u>:

1) A survey of motorists carried out in London concluded that 85% of the British people drive Black Cabs.

2) Two surveys carried out on the same street corner asked, "Do you believe in God?" One found 90% of people didn't and the other found 90% of people did. The reason for the discrepancy? — one was carried out at 11 pm Saturday night and the other at 10.15 am Sunday morning.

3) A telephone survey carried out in the evening asked, "What do you usually do after work or school?" It found that 80% of the population usually stay in and watch TV. A street survey conducted at the same time found that only 30% usually stay in and watch TV. Astonishing.

<u>Other cases are less obvious</u>:
In a telephone poll, 100 people were asked if they use the train regularly and 20% said yes. Does this mean 20% of the population regularly use the train?

<u>ANSWER</u>: <u>Probably not</u>. There are <u>several things wrong with this sampling technique</u>:
    1) <u>First and worst</u>: the sample is <u>far too small</u>. <u>At least 1000</u> would be more like it.
    2) What about people who don't have their own phone, e.g. students, tenants, etc.
    3) What time of day was it done? When might regular train users be in or out?
    4) Which part or parts of the region would you telephone?
    5) If the results were to represent, say, the whole country,
       <u>stratified sampling</u> would be essential.

The Acid Test:
LEARN the names and descriptions of the <u>three sampling techniques</u> and remember the bad sampling techniques.

1) A survey was done to investigate the average age of cars on Britain's roads by standing on a motorway bridge and noting the registration of the first 200 cars. Give three reasons why this is a poor sampling technique, and suggest a better approach.

Time Series

Time Series — Measure the Same Thing over a Period of Time

A time series is what you get if you measure the same thing at a number of different times.

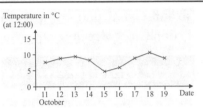
Temperature in °C (at 12:00)

EXAMPLE: Measuring the temperature in your greenhouse at 12 o'clock each day gives you a time series — other examples might be profit figures, crime figures or rainfall.

THE RETAIL PRICE INDEX (RPI) IS A TIME SERIES: Every month, the prices of loads of items (same ones each month) — are combined to get an index number called the RPI, which is a kind of average. As goods get more expensive, this index number gets higher and higher. So when you see on TV that inflation this month is 2.5%, what it actually means is that the RPI is increasing at an annual rate of 2.5%.

Seasonality — The Same Basic Pattern

This is when there's a definite pattern that **REPEATS ITSELF** every so often. This is called **SEASONALITY** and the *"so often"* is called the **PERIOD**.

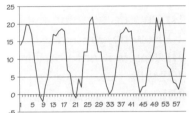

To find the **PERIOD**, measure **PEAK TO PEAK** (or trough to trough).

This series has a *period of 12 months*. There are a few irregularities, so the pattern isn't exactly the same every 12 months, but it's about right.

Trend — Ignoring the Wrinkles

This time series has lots of random fluctuations; but there's a definite upwards *trend*.

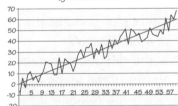

The pink line is the trend line. It's straight, so this is a *linear* trend.

Moving Average — Smooths Out the Seasonality

It's easier to spot a trend if you can 'get rid of' the seasonality and some of the irregularities.

One way to smooth a series is to use a *moving average*.

This is a time series that definitely looks periodic — but it's difficult to tell if there's a trend.

The period is 12, so you use 12 values for the moving average:

... but plot the moving average (in pink — must be pink — that's dead important)...

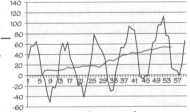

...and you can easily see the *upward trend*.

HOW TO FIND A MOVING AVERAGE:

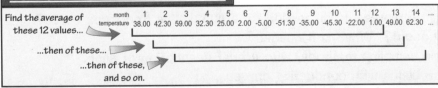

Find the average of these 12 values...

month	1	2	3	4	5	6	7	8	9	10	11	12	13	14	...
temperature	38.00	42.30	59.00	32.30	25.00	2.00	-5.00	-51.30	-35.00	-45.30	-22.00	1.00	49.00	62.30	...

...then of these...

...then of these, and so on.

The Acid Test:
LEARN the words TIME SERIES, SEASONALITY, PERIOD, TREND, MOVING AVERAGE. Cover the page and write a description of each.

1) My town's rainfall is measured every month for 20 yrs and graphed. There's a rough pattern, which repeats itself every 4 months. a) What is the period of this time series? b) Describe how to calculate a moving average.

Revision Summary for Module One

Here's the really fun page. The inevitable list of straight-down-the-middle questions to test how much you know. Remember, these questions will sort out (quicker than anything else can) exactly what you _know_ and what you _don't_. And that's exactly what revision is all about, don't forget: <u>find out what you DON'T know</u> and then learn it <u>until you do</u>. Enjoy.

Keep learning these basic facts until you know them

1) Write down the definitions of mean, median, mode and range.
2) What is the Golden Rule for finding the above for a set of data?
3) How should you tackle all probability questions?
4) Write down four important facts about tree diagrams.
5) Draw a general tree diagram and put all the features on it.
6) There are four other important things to know about probability. What are they?
7) Write down eight important details about frequency tables.
8) What are the class boundaries in a grouped frequency table?
9) How do you find the mid-interval values and what do you use them for?
10) How do you _estimate_ the mean from a grouped frequency table?
11) Why is it not possible to find the exact value of the mean from a grouped frequency table?
12) Write down four key points about cumulative frequency tables.
13) Draw a typical cumulative frequency curve, and indicate on it exactly where the median etc. are to be found.
14) Draw a box plot underneath your cumulative frequency curve from question 13.
15) What is a histogram?
16) What is the difference between one of these and a regular bar chart?
17) What are the three steps of the method for tackling all histograms?
18) Write down the formula for frequency density.
19) What is a scatter graph?
20) What does a scatter graph illustrate? What is the fancy word for this?
21) Draw three examples to illustrate the three main types.
22) What is the meaning of dispersion?
23) Can you deduce anything about the dispersion of a set of data from the shape of the histogram?
24) How do you estimate the mean from looking at a histogram?
25) Draw two histograms, one showing high dispersion, the other showing tight distribution.
26) Give examples of real data that might match each histogram.
27) Do cumulative frequency curves tell us anything about dispersion?
28) Draw two contrasting cumulative frequency curves.
29) Give an example of what these curves might represent and say what the significant difference between the two things will be.
30) Which numerical figure represents dispersion on a cumulative frequency curve?
31) What is sampling all about? When is it needed?
32) Name the three main sampling methods, with a brief description of each.
33) List five common problems with conducting surveys.
34) Which one of these is NOT a time series?
    a) measuring the temperature in 20 different countries at 12:00 today, GMT,
    b) measuring the temperature in Britain at 12:00 every day for 100 days,
    c) the Retail Price Index.
35) How can you find out if a seasonal time series has an overall trend?

Squares, Cubes and Negative Numbers

1) SQUARE NUMBERS:

They're called **SQUARE NUMBERS** because they're like the *areas* of this pattern of squares:

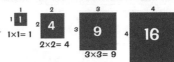

(1×1) (2×2) (3×3) (4×4) (5×5) (6×6) (7×7) (8×8) (9×9) (10×10) (11×11) (12×12) (13×13) (14×14) (15×15)

| 1 | 4 | 9 | 16 | 25 | 36 | 49 | 64 | 81 | 100 | 121 | 144 | 169 | 196 | 225... |

3   5   7   9   11   13   15   17   19   21   23   25   27   29

Note that the <u>DIFFERENCES</u> between the <u>square numbers</u> are all the <u>ODD</u> numbers.

2) CUBE NUMBERS:

They're called *CUBE NUMBERS* because they're like the *volumes* of this pattern of *cubes*.

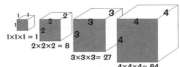

(1x1x1) (2x2x2) (3x3x3) (4x4x4) (5x5x5) (6x6x6) (7x7x7) (8x8x8) (9x9x9) (10x10x10)...

| 1 | 8 | 27 | 64 | 125 | 216 | 343 | 512 | 729 | 1000... |

3) SQUARE ROOTS:

"<u>Squared</u>" means "<u>times by itself</u>": $P^2 = P \times P$
— SQUARE ROOT is the <u>reverse process</u>.

The best way to think of it is this:

> ### "Square Root" means
> ### "What Number Times by Itself gives...?"

EXAMPLE: "<u>Find the square root of 49</u>" (i.e. "Find $\sqrt{49}$" or "Find $49^{\frac{1}{2}}$")
To do this you should say it as: "<u>What number TIMES BY ITSELF gives... 49?</u>"
Now, if you learn the number sequences above, then of course you'll know instantly that the answer is 7.

Estimating Square Roots

Looks horrible — but it's OK if you know your square numbers.

> 1) Find the TWO SQUARE NUMBERS EITHER SIDE of the number in question.
> 2) Find the SQUARE ROOTS and pick a SENSIBLE NUMBER IN BETWEEN.

EXAMPLE: "<u>Estimate $\sqrt{85}$ without using a calculator.</u>"

① The square numbers either side of 85 are *81* and *100*.

② The square roots are 9 and 10, so $\sqrt{85}$ must be <u>between 9 and 10</u>.

But 85 is much nearer 81 than 100, so $\sqrt{85}$ must be much <u>nearer 9 than 10</u>. So pick *9.1, 9.2 or 9.3*.
(The answer's actually 9.2195... if you're interested.)

4) NEGATIVE NUMBERS:

<u>Negative</u> numbers crop up everywhere, so you need to <u>learn this rule</u> for how to deal with them.

+	+	makes	+
+	–	makes	–
–	+	makes	–
–	–	makes	+

> **1) Multiplying or dividing:** e.g. $-2 \times 3 = \underline{-6}$, $-8 \div -2 = \underline{+4}$ $-4p \times -2 = \underline{+8p}$

> **2) Two signs are together:** e.g. $5 - -4 = 5+4 = \underline{9}$ $4 + -6 - -7 = 4 - 6 + 7 = \underline{5}$

The Acid Test:

<u>LEARN</u> the <u>sequences of squares and cubes</u>, and the <u>rule</u> for <u>negative</u> numbers. Then turn the page and write it all down.

1) From this list of numbers: 8, 81, 27, 25, 125, 36, 1, 64, 1000, 225
write down a) all the <u>square</u> numbers   b) all the <u>cube</u> numbers

2) Calculate the following: a) $\sqrt{200}$ b) If $4 \times r^2 = 36$, find r   c) $120 \div -40$

Prime Numbers

1) *Basically, PRIME Numbers don't divide by anything*

And that's the best way to think of them. (Strictly, they divide by themselves and 1.)
So Prime Numbers are all the numbers that DON'T come up in Times Tables:

| 2 | 3 | 5 | 7 | 11 | 13 | 17 | 19 | 23 | 29 | 31 | 37 | ... |

As you can see, they're an awkward-looking bunch (that's because they don't divide by anything!). For example:

| The only numbers that multiply to give 7 are | 1×7 |
| The only numbers that multiply to give 31 are | 1×31 |

In fact the only way to get ANY PRIME NUMBER is $1 \times$ ITSELF

2) *They All End in 1, 3, 7 or 9*

1) 1 is NOT a prime number

2) The first four prime numbers are 2, 3, 5 and 7

3) 2 and 5 are the EXCEPTIONS because all the rest end in 1, 3, 7 or 9

4) But NOT ALL numbers ending in 1, 3, 7 or 9 are primes, as shown here:
(Only the *circled ones* are *primes*)

② ③ ⑤ ⑦
⑪ ⑬ ⑰ ⑲
21 ㉓ 27 ㉙
㉛ 33 ㊲ 39
㊹ ㊸ ㊼ 49
51 ㊽ 57 ㊾
㊶ 63 ㊿ 69

3) *How to Find Prime Numbers* — *a very simple method*

For a chosen number to be a *prime*:

1) It must end in either 1, 3, 7 or 9.
2) It WON'T DIVIDE by any of the primes below the value of its own square root.

If something like this comes up on the non-calculator paper, you'll have to start by estimating the square root — see P. 15.

Example "Decide whether or not 233 is a prime number."

1) Does it end in either 1, 3, 7 or 9? Yes
2) Find its square root: $\sqrt{233} = 15.264...$
3) List all primes (apart from 2 and 5) which are less than this square root: 3, 7, 11 and 13
4) Divide all of these primes into the number under test:

233 ÷ 3 = 77.6667   233 ÷ 7 = 33.2857
233 ÷ 11 = 21.181818   233 ÷ 13 = 17.923077

5) Since none of these divide cleanly into 233 then it IS a prime number. Easy Peasy.

The Acid Test: LEARN the main points in ALL 3 SECTIONS above.

Now cover the page and write down everything you've just learned.
1) Write down the first 15 prime numbers (without looking them up).
2) Find all the prime numbers between a) 100 and 110 b) 200 and 210 c) 500 and 510

Multiples, Factors and Prime Factors

Multiples

The **MULTIPLES** of a number are simply its **TIMES TABLE**:

E.g. the <u>multiples of 13</u> are   13   26   39   52   65   78   91   104   ...

Factors

The **FACTORS** of a number are all the numbers that **DIVIDE INTO IT EXACTLY**. There is a special way to find them:

Example 1:   *"Find ALL the factors of 24"*

Start off with 1 x the number itself, then try 2 x, then 3 x and so on, listing the pairs in rows like this. Try each one in turn and put a dash if it doesn't divide exactly. Eventually, when you get a number *repeated*, you *stop*.

> So the <u>FACTORS OF 24</u> are   <u>1,2,3,4,6,8,12,24</u>

(Increasing by 1 each time)

1 x 24
2 x 12
3 x 8
4 x 6
5 x -
6 x 4

This method guarantees you find them **ALL**. And don't forget 1 and 24!

Example 2:   *"Find the factors of 64"*

<u>Check each one in turn</u>, to see if it divides or not. Use your calculator if you are not totally confident.

1 x 64
2 x 32
3 x –
4 x 16
5 x –
6 x –
7 x –
8 x 8   — The 8 has <u>repeated</u> so <u>stop here</u>.

> So the <u>FACTORS of 64</u> are   <u>1,2,4,8,16,32,64</u>

Finding Prime Factors — The Factor Tree

<u>Any number</u> can be broken down into <u>a string of PRIME NUMBERS all multiplied together</u> — this is called <u>"Expressing it as a product of prime factors"</u>, and to be honest it's pretty tedious – but it's in the Exam, <u>and it's not difficult so long as you know what it is</u>.

The mildly entertaining <u>"Factor Tree" method</u> is best, where you start at the top and split your number off into factors as shown. Each time you get a prime you ring it and you finally end up with all the prime factors, which you can then arrange in order.

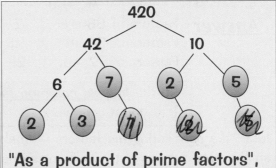

"As a product of prime factors",
420 = 2×12×2×8×5×5×7×7
2 × 3 × 7 × 5 × 2

The Acid Test:

LEARN what <u>Multiples, Factors and Prime Factors</u> are, **AND HOW TO FIND THEM.** <u>Turn over and write it down.</u>

1) Express as a product of prime factors: a) 990   b) 160.

LCM and HCF

Two big fancy names, but don't be put off — they're both _dead easy_.

LCM — "Lowest Common Multiple"

"Least Common Multiple" — sure, it sounds kind of complicated but _all it means is this_:

> The **SMALLEST** number that will **DIVIDE BY**
> **ALL** the numbers in question.

Method
1) _LIST_ the _MULTIPLES_ of _ALL_ the numbers.
2) Find the _SMALLEST_ one that's in _ALL the lists_.
3) Easy peasy, innit.

Example _Find the least common multiple (LCM) of 6 and 7._

Answer Multiples of 6 are: 6, 12, 18, 24, 30, 36, (42,) 48, 54, 60, 66, ...
Multiples of 7 are: 7, 14, 21, 28, 35, (42,) 49, 56, 63, 70, 77, ...

> So the _least common multiple_ (LCM) of 6 and 7 is _42_.
> Told you it was easy.

HCF — "Highest Common Factor"

"Highest Common Factor" — all it means is _this_:

> The **BIGGEST** number that will **DIVIDE INTO**
> **ALL** the numbers in question.

Method
1) _LIST_ the _FACTORS_ of _ALL_ the numbers.
2) Find the _BIGGEST_ one that's in _ALL the lists_.
3) Easy peasy, innit.

Example _Find the highest common factor (HCF) of 36, 54 and 72._

Answer Factors of 36 are: 1, 2, 3, 4, 6, 9, 12, (18,) 36
Factors of 54 are: 1, 2, 3, 6, 9, (18,) 27, 54
Factors of 72 are: 1, 2, 3, 4, 6, 8, 9, 12, (18,) 24, 36, 72

> So the _highest common factor_ (HCF) of 36, 54 and 72 is _18_.
> Told you it was easy.

Just _take care_ listing the factors — make sure you use the _proper method_ (as shown on the previous page) or you'll miss one and blow the whole thing out of the water.

The Acid Test:
LEARN what _LCM_ and _HCF_ are, AND HOW TO FIND THEM. _Turn over and write it down_.

Then try these _without the notes_:
1) List the first 10 multiples of 7 and of 9. What is their Least Common Multiple (LCM)?
2) List _all_ the factors of 36 and 84.   What is their Highest Common Factor (HCF)?

Powers and Roots

Powers are a very useful shorthand: $2 \times 2 \times 2 \times 2 \times 2 \times 2 \times 2 = 2^7$ ("two to the power 7")

That bit is easy to remember. Unfortunately, there are TEN SPECIAL RULES for Powers that are not tremendously exciting, but you do need to know them for the Exam:

Also in module 5:

The Seven Easy Rules:

1) When **MULTIPLYING**, you **ADD THE POWERS**.   e.g. $3^4 \times 3^6 = 3^{4+6} = 3^{10}$

2) When **DIVIDING**, you **SUBTRACT THE POWERS**.   e.g. $5^6 \div 5^2 = 5^{6-2} = 5^4$

3) When **RAISING one power to another**, you **MULTIPLY THEM**.   e.g. $(3^2)^4 = 3^{2 \times 4} = 3^8$

4) $X^1 = X$ **ANYTHING** to the **POWER 1** is just **ITSELF**.   e.g. $3^1 = 3$, $6 \times 6^3 = 6^4$

5) $X^0 = 1$ **ANYTHING** to the **POWER 0** is just **ONE**.   e.g. $5^0 = 1$ $67^0 = 1$

6) $1^x = 1$ **1 TO ANY POWER** is **STILL JUST 1**.   e.g. $1^{23} = 1$ $1^{89} = 1$ $1^2 = 1$

7) **FRACTIONS** — Apply Power to <u>both TOP and BOTTOM</u>.   e.g. $\left(1\frac{3}{5}\right)^3 = \left(\frac{8}{5}\right)^3 = \frac{8^3}{5^3} = \frac{512}{125}$

The Three Tricky Rules:

8) NEGATIVE Powers —Turn it UPSIDE DOWN

People do have quite a bit of difficulty remembering this.

Whenever you see a negative power you're supposed to immediately think:

"Aha, that means turn it the other way up and make the power positive."

<u>LIKE THIS:</u>   e.g. $7^{-2} = \frac{1}{7^2} = \frac{1}{49}$ $\left(\frac{3}{5}\right)^{-2} = \left(\frac{5}{3}\right)^{+2} = \frac{5^2}{3^2} = \frac{25}{9}$

9) FRACTIONAL POWERS mean one thing: ROOTS

e.g. $25^{\frac{1}{2}} = \sqrt{25} = 5$

> The Power ½ means <u>Square Root</u>,
> The Power ⅓ means <u>Cube Root</u>,
> The Power ¼ means <u>Fourth Root</u> etc.

$64^{\frac{1}{3}} = \sqrt[3]{64} = 4$

$81^{\frac{1}{4}} = \sqrt[4]{81} = 3$

Watch out with a <u>negative fraction</u> like 49 $^{-\frac{1}{2}}$. This is $\frac{1}{\sqrt{49}} = \frac{1}{7}$. (People get mixed up and think that the minus is the square root, and forget to turn it upside down as well.)

10) TWO-STAGE FRACTIONAL POWERS

They really like putting these in Exam questions so learn the method:

With fractional powers like $64^{\frac{5}{6}}$ always **SPLIT THE FRACTION** into <u>a ROOT and a POWER</u>,

and do them in that order: **ROOT** first, then **POWER**: $64^{\frac{5}{6}} = \left(64^{\frac{1}{6}}\right)^5 = \left(\sqrt[6]{64}\right)^5 = 2^5 = 32$

Square Roots can be Positive or Negative — Shock news just in...

It's true. If you multiply a negative number by itself, you get a positive number:

$(-2)^2 = (-2) \times (-2) = 4$ But $2^2 = 4$ as well. (What's going on...)

It's actually quite simple: $\sqrt{4} = +2 \text{ or } -2$

... and that goes for all square roots.

Whenever you get a <u>positive square root</u>, you also get a <u>negative one</u>.

The Acid Test:

LEARN ALL TEN *Exciting Rules on this page. Then* **TURN OVER** *and write them all down with examples.* **Keep trying till you can.**

1) Simplify: a) $3^2 \times 3^6$ b) $4^3 / 4^2$ c) $(8^3)^4$ d) $(3^2 \times 3^3 \times 1^6)/3^5$ e) $7^3 \times 7 \times 7^2$

2) Evaluate   a) $(\frac{1}{4})^{-3}$ b) 25^{-2} c) $25^{-\frac{1}{2}}$ d) $\left(\frac{27}{216}\right)^{-\frac{1}{3}}$ e) $625^{\frac{3}{4}}$ f) $125^{-\frac{2}{3}}$

3) Use your Calculator buttons (P.32) to find: a) 5.2^{24} b) $40^{\frac{3}{4}}$ c) $\sqrt[5]{200}$

Manipulating Surds and Use of π

<u>RATIONAL NUMBERS</u> The vast majority of numbers are rational. They are always either:

> 1) A whole number (either positive (+ve), or negative (−ve))   e.g. 4, -5, -12.
> 2) A fraction p/q, where p and q are whole numbers (+ve or −ve) e.g. ¼, -½, ¾.
> 3) A terminating or recurring decimal, e.g. 0.125   0.3333333333...   0.143143143143..

<u>IRRATIONAL NUMBERS</u> are messy!

> 1) They are always <u>NEVER-ENDING NON-REPEATING DECIMALS</u>. π is irrational.
> 2) A *good source* of <u>IRRATIONAL NUMBERS</u> is <u>SQUARE ROOTS AND CUBE ROOTS</u>.

Manipulating Surds

It sounds like something to do with controlling difficult children, but it isn't. Surds are expressions with irrational square roots in them. You <u>MUST USE THEM</u> if they ask you for an <u>EXACT</u> answer. There are a few simple rules to learn:

1) $\sqrt{a} \times \sqrt{b} = \sqrt{ab}$ e.g. $\sqrt{2} \times \sqrt{3} = \sqrt{2 \times 3} = \sqrt{6}$ — also $(\sqrt{b})^2 = b$, fairly obviously

2) $\sqrt{a}/\sqrt{b} = \sqrt{a/b}$ e.g. $\sqrt{8}/\sqrt{2} = \sqrt{8/2} = \sqrt{4} = 2$

3) $\sqrt{a} + \sqrt{b}$ — <u>NOTHING DOING</u>...   (in other words it is definitely NOT $\sqrt{a+b}$)

4) $(a + \sqrt{b})^2 = (a + \sqrt{b})(a + \sqrt{b}) = a^2 + 2a\sqrt{b} + b$ (NOT just $a^2 + (\sqrt{b})^2$)

5) $(a + \sqrt{b})(a - \sqrt{b}) = a^2 + a\sqrt{b} - a\sqrt{b} - (\sqrt{b})^2 = a^2 - b$

6) Express $3/\sqrt{5}$ in the form $a\sqrt{5}/b$ where a and b are whole numbers.
   To do this you must *"<u>RATIONALISE the denominator</u>"*, which just means multiplying top and bottom by $\sqrt{5}$: $\dfrac{3\sqrt{5}}{\sqrt{5}\sqrt{5}} = \dfrac{3\sqrt{5}}{5}$ so a = 3 and b = 5.

7) If you want an *exact* answer, <u>LEAVE THE SURDS IN</u>. As soon as you go using that calculator, you'll get a *big fat rounding error* — and you'll get the answer <u>WRONG</u>. Don't say I didn't warn you...

> <u>***Example:***</u> A square has an area of 15 cm². Find the length of one of its sides.
> <u>***Answer:***</u>   The length of a side is $\sqrt{15}$ cm.
>   If you <u>have a calculator</u>, then you can work out $\sqrt{15}$ = 3.8729833...cm.
>   If you're working <u>without a calculator</u>, or are asked to give an <u>EXACT</u> answer,
>   then just write: $\sqrt{15}$ cm. That's all you have to do.

Exact calculations using π

π is another <u>irrational</u> number that often comes up in calculations, e.g. in finding the area of a circle. Most of the time you can use the nifty little π button on your calculator. But if you're asked to give an <u>exact</u> answer or, worse still, do the calculation <u>without a calculator</u>, just <u>leave</u> the π symbol in the calculation.

> <u>***Example:***</u> Find the area of a circle with radius 4 cm, without using a calculator.
> <u>***Answer:***</u>   The area = $\pi r^2 = \pi \times 4^2 = 16\pi$ cm².

The Acid Test:

LEARN the <u>7 rules</u> for <u>manipulating surds</u>, then <u>turn over and write it all down</u>.

Simplify 1) $(1 + \sqrt{2})^2 - (1 - \sqrt{2})^2$ 2) $(1 + \sqrt{2})^2 - (2\sqrt{2} - \sqrt{2})^2$

Fractions and Decimals

Converting Fractions to Decimals — Just DIVIDE

Just remember that " / " means " ÷ ", so ¼ means 1 ÷ 4 = 0.25.

The _denominator_ (bottom number) of a fraction, tells you if it'll be a _recurring_ or _terminating decimal_ when you convert it. _Recurring_ decimals have a _pattern_ of numbers which repeats itself forever, e.g. ⅓ is the decimal 0.333... . _Terminating_ decimals are _finite_, e.g. ¹⁄₂₀ is the decimal 0.05.

For prime factors see p.17

FRACTION	⅕	¹⁄₁₂₅	½	¹⁄₂₀		⅐	¹⁄₃₅	⅓	⅙
EQUIVALENT DECIMAL	0.2	0.008	0.5	0.05		0.142857	0.0285714	0.3333	0.16666

only _prime_ factors: 2 & 5

also _other_ prime factors

Fractions where the denominator has _prime factors_ of _only 2 or 5_ will give _terminating_ decimals. All _other fractions_ will give _recurring decimals_.

Converting Decimals to Fractions

— It's a simple rule, so work it out for yourself!

0.6 = ⁶⁄₁₀,   0.3 = ³⁄₁₀,   0.7 = ⁷⁄₁₀,   0.X = ˣ⁄₁₀, etc.

0.12 = ¹²⁄₁₀₀,   0.78 = ⁷⁸⁄₁₀₀,   0.45 = ⁴⁵⁄₁₀₀,   0.05 = ⁵⁄₁₀₀, etc.

0.345 = ³⁴⁵⁄₁₀₀₀,   0.908 = ⁹⁰⁸⁄₁₀₀₀,   0.024 = ²⁴⁄₁₀₀₀,   0.XYZ = ˣʸᶻ⁄₁₀₀₀, etc.

These can then be _cancelled down_.

The above method is all well and good for converting terminating decimals into fractions, but what about recurring ones? All you need is the lovely method below.

Turning Recurring Decimals into Fractions

There's two ways you can do it:
1) by _UNDERSTANDING_   2) by just _LEARNING THE RESULT_.   Both ways are cool.

The Understanding Method:

1) Find the _length_ of the _repeating sequence_ and _multiply_ by 10, 100, 1000, 10 000 or whatever to move it all up past the decimal point by _one full repeated lump_:

E.g. 0.234234234... × 1000 = 234.234234..

2) _Subtract the original number_, r, from the new one (which in this case is 1000r)
i.e. 1000r − r = 234.234234... − 0.234234...
giving: 999r = 234

3) Then just _DIVIDE_ to leave r: r = ²³⁴⁄₉₉₉ , and cancel if possible: r = ²⁶⁄₁₁₁

The "Just Learning The Result" Method:

The fraction always has the repeating unit on the top and the same number of nines on the bottom — easy as that. Look at these and marvel at the elegant simplicity of it.

0.4444444 = 4/9   0.34343434 = 34/99
0.124124124 = 124/999   0.14561456 = 1456/9999

Always check if it will _CANCEL DOWN_ of course, e.g. 0.363636.... = 36/99 = 4/11

The Acid Test:
LEARN how to tell whether a _fraction_ will be a _terminating_ or _recurring_ decimal, and _all_ the _methods_ above. Then _turn over and write it all down._

1) Express 0.142857142857.... as a fraction. 2) Convert 0.035 into a fraction and cancel it down.

Decimals and Reciprocals

Decimals without the calculator aren't that bad. Learn these neat tricks and you're laughing.

Multiplying Decimals — Take out the Decimal Point

It might sound weird, but leave out decimal points until the end — LEARN THESE STEPS:

1) Do the multiplication using WHOLE NUMBERS — leave out the decimal points.

2) Count the total number of digits that come after the decimal points in the question.

3) Put the same number of digits after the decimal point in the answer.

EXAMPLE: "Work out 3.72 x 2.4"

372 x 24 = 8928   (You'll have to work this out the good old fashioned way.)

3.72 x 2.4 has 3 digits after the decimal points, so the answer is 8.928

Dividing Decimals — just like Normal Division

There's THREE EASY STEPS to learn for this too:

1) Keep the decimal point in the number you're dividing.

2) Do the division as normal, dividing into digits after the decimal point in the same way.

3) When you've finished the division, put a decimal point in the answer, DIRECTLY ABOVE the decimal point in the number you divided.

EXAMPLE: "Work out 325.8 ÷ 6"

$$\begin{array}{r} 5 \\ 6\overline{)32^25.8} \end{array} \longrightarrow \begin{array}{r} 5\,4.\,3 \\ 6\overline{)32^25.^18} \end{array}$$

The decimal point in the answer goes above the other decimal point.

3 is too small, but 32 ÷ 6 = 5 with 2 left over (remainder 2)

Reciprocals — "One Over" a Number

No, a government health warning isn't necessary for reciprocals, they aren't that nasty...

1) The reciprocal of a number is 1 divided by that number, e.g. the reciprocal of 5 is $\frac{1}{5}$.

2) You can't divide by zero, so zero has no reciprocal.

3) Multiply any number by its reciprocal and you get 1, e.g. $5 \times \frac{1}{5} = 1$

Turn Fractions Upside Down to get the Reciprocal

1) You get the reciprocal of a fraction by turning it upside down, e.g. the reciprocal of $\frac{2}{3}$ is $\frac{3}{2}$, and the reciprocal of $\frac{5}{8}$ is $\frac{8}{5}$.

2) A unit fraction has 1 on the top, e.g. $\frac{1}{2}$, $\frac{1}{3}$, $\frac{1}{23}$. The reciprocal of a unit fraction is just the number on the bottom, e.g. the reciprocal of $\frac{1}{3}$ is 3.

The Acid Test:

1) Work out 3.2 × 2067   2) Work out 162.4 ÷ 7   3) What's the reciprocal of a) 12, b) $\frac{1}{4}$

Standard Index Form

Standard Form and Standard Index Form are the SAME THING.
So remember both of these names as well as what it actually is:

Ordinary Number: 4,300,000   In Standard Form: 4.3   X 10^6

Standard form is only really useful for writing VERY BIG or VERY SMALL numbers in a
more convenient way, e.g.

56,000,000,000 would be 5.6×10^{10} in standard form.
0.000 000 003 45 would be 3.45×10^{-9} in standard form.

but ANY NUMBER can be written in standard form and *you need to know how to do it*:

What it Actually is:

A number written in standard form must ALWAYS be in EXACTLY this form:

$$A \times 10^n$$

This *number* must *always*
be BETWEEN 1 AND 10.

*(The fancy way of saying this is:
" 1 ≤ A < 10" — they sometimes write that
in Exam questions — don't let it put you off,
just remember what it means.)*

This number is just
the NUMBER OF
PLACES
*the Decimal Point
moves*.

Learn The Three Rules:

1) The front number must always be BETWEEN 1 AND 10.

2) The power of 10, n, is purely: HOW FAR THE D.P. MOVES.

3) n is +ve for BIG numbers,   n is –ve for SMALL numbers.

(This is much better than rules based on which way the D.P. moves.)

Two Very Simple Examples:

1) *"Express 35 600 in standard form."*

METHOD:
*1) Move the D.P. until 35 600 becomes 3.56 ("1 ≤ A <10").
2) The D.P. has moved 4 places so n=4, giving: 10^4.
3) 35600 is a BIG number so n is +4, not –4.*

ANSWER:

3.5 6 0 0.

= 3.56 x 10^4

2) *"Express 0.000623 in standard form."*

METHOD:
*1) The D.P. must move 4 places to give 6.23 ("1 ≤ A <10").
2) So the power of 10 is 4.
3) Since 0.000623 is a SMALL NUMBER it must be 10^{-4} not 10^{+4}.*

ANSWER:

0.000623

= 6.23 × 10^{-4}

Standard Index Form

Standard Form and The Calculator

People usually manage all that stuff about moving the decimal point OK (*apart from always forgetting that FOR A BIG NUMBER it's "ten to the power +ve something" and FOR A SMALL NUMBER it's "ten to the power –ve something"*), but when it comes to doing standard form on a *calculator* it's invariably a sorry saga of confusion and ineptitude.

But it's not so bad really — you just have to learn it, that's all.....

1) Entering Standard Form Numbers EXP

The button you MUST USE to put standard form numbers into the calculator is the EXP

(or EE) button — but DON'T go pressing X   10 as well, like a lot of people do,

because that makes it WRONG.

Example:

"Enter 2.67 × 10^{11} into the calculator"

Just press: 2.67   EXP   11 and the display will be 2.67^{11}

Note that you ONLY PRESS the EXP (or EE) button — you DON'T press X or 10 .

2) Reading Standard Form Numbers:

The big thing you have to remember when you write any standard form number from the calculator display is to put the "×10" in yourself. DON'T just write down what it says on the display.

Example: *"Write down the number 7.986^{05} as a finished answer."*

As a finished answer this must be written as 7.986 × 10^5.

It is NOT 7.986^5 so DON'T write it down like that — YOU have to put the × 10^n in yourself, even though it isn't shown in the display at all. *That's the bit people forget*.

Calculating with Standard Form

Once you've mastered *expressing* numbers in standard form, you need to make sure you can *calculate* with them, *without* using your calculator. **LEARN THE METHOD BELOW.**

Example: *"Calculate (2.5 × 10^7) × (6 × 10^3). Write your answer in standard form."*

METHOD:
1) Multiply the FRONT NUMBER from the first expression by the front number from the second.
2) Multiply the first POWER OF 10 by the second.
3) Make sure your answer is in STANDARD FORM (the front number is between 1 and 10).

Answer: *For a reminder about dealing with powers see p.19*

$2.5 × 6 = 15$
$10^7 × 10^3 = 10^{10}$
$15 × 10^{10}$ isn't in standard form since $15 > 10$
$15 × 10^{10} = \underline{1.5 × 10^{11}}$

(To divide expressions, use the same method but replace "multiply" with "divide".)

The Acid Test: LEARN the Two Calculator Methods and the Three Rules then turn over and write them down.

1) Express 958,000 in standard index form.   2) And the same for 0.00018
3) Express 4.56 × 10^3 as an ordinary number.
4) Write the answer to the following in standard form: (3.2 × 10^{12}) ÷ (1.6 × 10^{-9})

Basic Algebra

Use the Number Line for Negative Numbers

The number line comes in handy when you're adding and subtracting like terms:

Use the number line when **ADDING OR SUBTRACTING**.

THE NUMBER LINE

+6X   +4X

-10 -9 -8 -7 -6 -5 -4 -3 -2 -1 0 1 2 3 4 5 6 7 8 9 10

-3X   -8X

Example:
"Simplify: 4X - 8X - 3X + 6X"   So   4X - 8X - 3X + 6X = _-1X_ = (-X)

Letters Multiplied Together

Watch out for these combinations of letters in algebra that regularly catch people out:

1) abc means a×b×c.   The ×'s are often left out to make it clearer.

2) gn^2 means g×n×n.   Note that only the n is squared, not the g as well. E.g. πr^2

3) $(gn)^2$ means g×g×n×n.   The brackets mean that **BOTH** letters are squared.

4) $p(q - r)^3$ means p × (q – r) × (q – r) × (q – r).   Only the brackets get cubed.

5) -3^2 is a bit ambiguous.   It should either be written $(-3)^2 = 9$, or $-(3^2) = -9$

Terms

1) **A TERM IS A COLLECTION OF NUMBERS, LETTERS AND BRACKETS, ALL MULTIPLIED/DIVIDED TOGETHER.**

2) **TERMS are SEPARATED BY + AND − SIGNS** E.g. $4x^2 - 3py - 5 + 3p$

3) TERMS always have a + or − **ATTACHED TO THE FRONT OF THEM**

4) E.g.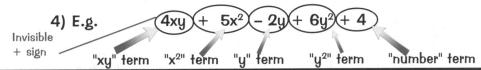

Invisible + sign

"xy" term   "x²" term   "y" term   "y²" term   "number" term

SIMPLIFYING   — or "Collecting Like Terms"

EXAMPLE: Simplify   2x – 4 + 5x + 6

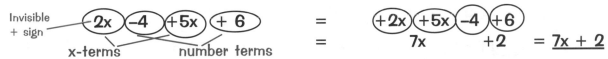

Invisible + sign

x-terms   number terms

$= 7x + 2$

7x   +2

1) Put bubbles round each term — be sure you capture the +/– sign IN FRONT of each.
2) Then you can move the bubbles into the best order so that LIKE TERMS are together.
3) "LIKE TERMS" have exactly the same combination of letters, e.g. x-terms or xy-terms.
4) Combine LIKE TERMS using the NUMBER LINE.

The Acid Test:

1) Work out: a) –4 × –3   b) –4 + –5 + 3   c) (3X + –2X – 4X) ÷ (2 + –5)

2) If m=2 and n=–3 work out: a) mn^2 b) $(mn)^3$ c) $m(4 + n)^2$ d) n^3 e) $3m^2n^3 + 2mn$

3) Simplify: a) 5x + 3y – 4 – 2y – x   b) 2xy + 4x – 3xy + 5y + 3y

Also in module 5:

Fractions

The Fraction Button: $a^{b}/_{c}$

Use this as much as possible in the calculator paper. It's very easy, so make sure you know how to use it — you'll lose a lot of marks if you don't:

1) To enter $\frac{1}{4}$ press [1] [$a^b/_c$] [4]
2) To enter $1\frac{3}{5}$ press [1] [$a^b/_c$] [3] [$a^b/_c$] [5]
3) To work out $\frac{1}{5}\times\frac{3}{4}$ press [1] [$a^b/_c$] [5] [X] [3] [$a^b/_c$] [4] [=]
4) To *reduce a fraction to its lowest terms* enter it and then press [=]
   e.g. $\frac{9}{12}$, [9] [$a^b/_c$] [12] [=] [3⌟4] $= \frac{3}{4}$
5) To convert between *mixed* and *top-heavy* fractions press [SHIFT] [$a^b/_c$]
   e.g. $2\frac{3}{8}$ [2] [$a^b/_c$] [3] [$a^b/_c$] [8] [=] [SHIFT] [$a^b/_c$] which gives $\frac{19}{8}$

Doing Fractions By Hand

You're not allowed to use your calculator in the Non-Calculator Exam (unsurprisingly). Frighteningly, you'll have to *do them "by hand"* instead, so learn these 5 basic rules:

1) Multiplying — easy.

Multiply top and bottom separately: $\frac{3}{5}\times\frac{4}{7}=\frac{3\times4}{5\times7}=\frac{12}{35}$

2) Dividing — quite easy.

Turn the *2nd fraction upside down* and then *multiply*: $\frac{3}{4}\div\frac{1}{3}=\frac{3}{4}\times\frac{3}{1}=\frac{3\times3}{4\times1}=\frac{9}{4}$

3) Cancelling down — easy.

Divide top and bottom by the same number, till they won't go any further: $\frac{12}{16}=\frac{6}{8}=\frac{3}{4}$

4) Adding/subtracting — fraught.

i) First get the bottom lines the same (get a "common denominator").

E.g. $\frac{2}{3}+\frac{1}{5}=\frac{2\times5}{3\times5}+\frac{1\times3}{5\times3}=\frac{10}{15}+\frac{3}{15}$ (multiply the top and bottom of each fraction by the same number)

ii) Add or subtract TOP LINES ONLY but *only if the bottom numbers are the same.*

e.g. $\frac{10}{15}+\frac{3}{15}=\frac{13}{15}$ or , $\frac{2}{6}+\frac{1}{6}=\frac{3}{6}$, $\frac{5}{7}-\frac{3}{7}=\frac{2}{7}$

5) Finding A FRACTION OF something — just multiply.

Multiply by the top, divide by the bottom: $\frac{9}{20}$ of £360 $= \frac{9}{20}\times £360=\frac{£3240}{20}=£162$

Finally — Checking.

ALWAYS check your answer.

The Acid Test:

LEARN the 5 features of the Fraction Button and the 5 Manual Methods, then turn over and write it all down.

1) With your calculator:
a) 1/2 x 3/4 b) 3/5 ÷ 2/9 c) 1/3 + 2/5 d) Find x: $2\frac{3}{5}=\frac{x}{5}$ e) Find y: $\frac{14}{98}=\frac{y}{7}$

2) By hand: a) 2/3 x 4/5 b) 4/5 ÷ 3/10 c) 5/8 – 2/6 d) Express 36/84 in its simplest form. e) $3\frac{1}{2}-2\frac{3}{4}$ f) $2\frac{1}{3}\times3\frac{1}{5}$ g) $2\frac{3}{5}\div1\frac{1}{10}$

Percentages

You shouldn't have any trouble with most percentage questions, especially types 1 and 2. However watch out for type 3 questions and make sure you know the proper method for doing them. "Percentage change" can also catch you out if you don't keep your wits about you.

Type 1   *"Find x% of y"* — e.g. Find 15% of £46 $\Rightarrow 0.15 \times 46 = \underline{£6.90}$

Type 2   *"Express x as a percentage of y"*
e.g. Give 40p as a percentage of £3.34 $\Rightarrow (40 \div 334) \times 100 = \underline{12\%}$

Type 3 — *IDENTIFIED BY NOT GIVING THE "ORIGINAL VALUE"*

These are the type most people get wrong – but only because they don't recognise them as a type 3 and don't apply this simple method:

Example: A house increases in value by 20% to £72,000. Find what it was worth <u>before</u> the rise.

Method

$\div 120$ £72,000 = 120%

£600 = 1%

$\times 100$ £60,000 = 100%

So the original price was £60,000

An INCREASE of 20% means that £72,000 represents *120% of the original* value. If it was a DROP of 20%, then we would put "£72,000 = <u>80%</u>" instead, and then divide by 80 on the LHS, instead of 120.

<u>Always set them out exactly like this example.</u> The trickiest bit is deciding the top % figure on the RHS — the 2nd and 3rd rows are <u>always</u> 1% and 100%.

Percentage Change

It is common to give a *change in value* as a *percentage*. This is the formula for doing so — LEARN IT, AND USE IT:

$$\text{PERCENTAGE CHANGE} = \frac{\text{CHANGE}}{\text{ORIGINAL}} \times 100$$

By "change", we could mean all sorts of things such as: "Profit", "loss", "appreciation", "depreciation", "increase", "decrease", "error", "discount", etc. For example,

$$\text{percentage profit} = \frac{\text{profit}}{\text{original}} \times 100$$

Note the great importance of using the ORIGINAL VALUE in this formula.

The Acid Test:
LEARN The details for TYPE 3 QUESTIONS and PERCENTAGE CHANGE, then <u>turn over and write it all down.</u>

1) A trader buys watches for £5 and sells them for £7. Find his profit as a percentage.
2) A car depreciates by 30% to £14,350. What was it worth before?
3) Find the percentage error in rounding 3.452 to 3.5. Give your answer to 2 DP.

AQA MODULAR MATHS — MODULE THREE

Compound Growth and Decay

This can also be called "Exponential" Growth or Decay.

The Formula

This topic is simple if you LEARN THIS FORMULA. If you don't, it's pretty well impossible:

$$N = N_0\left(1 + \frac{r}{100}\right)^n$$

New amount

Initial amount

Percentage change per day/hour/year

Number of days/hrs/yrs

Percentage Increase and Decrease

The $(1 + r/100)$ bit might look a bit confusing in the formula but in practise it's really easy:

E.g   5% increase will be 1.05   5% decrease will be 0.95 $(= 1 - 0.05)$
         26% increase will be 1.26   26% decrease will be 0.74 $(= 1 - 0.26)$

You can also combine increases and decreases:

E.g. A 20% increase in value a followed by a 20% decrease will be $1.2 \times 0.8 \times a$.
They don't cancel each other out.

3 Examples to show you how EASY it is:

1) *"A man invests £1000 in a savings account which pays 8% per annum. How much will there be after 6 years?"*

ANSWER: Usual formula (as above):   Amount $= 1000(1.08)^6 = $ £1586.87

Initial amount   8% increase   6 years

2) *"The activity of a radio-isotope falls by 12% every hour. If the initial activity is 800 counts per minute, what will it be after 7 hours?"*

ANSWER: Same old formula:

Activity $=$ Initial value$(1 - 12/100)^n$

Activity $= 800(1 - 0.12)^7 = 800 \times (0.88)^7 = $ 327 cpm

3) *"In a sample of bacteria, there are initially 500 cells and they increase in number by 15% each day. Find the formula relating the number of cells, n and the number of days, d."*

ANSWER: Well stone me, it's the same old easy-peasy compound increase formula again:

$n = n_0(1 + 0.15)^d$ or finished off: $n = 500 \times (1.15)^d$

The Acid Test:

LEARN THE FORMULA.   Also learn the 3 Examples. Then turn over and write it all down.

1) A colony of stick insects increases in number by 4% per week. Initially there are 30. How many will there be after 12 weeks?

2) The speed of a tennis ball rolled along a smooth floor falls by 16% every second. If the initial speed was 5 m/s, find the speed after 20 seconds. How long will it take to stop?

Ratios

The whole grisly subject of <u>RATIOS</u> gets a whole lot easier when you do this:

Treat RATIOS like FRACTIONS

So for the <u>RATIO</u> 3:4, you'd treat it as the <u>FRACTION</u> 3/4, which is 0.75 as a <u>DECIMAL</u>.

What the fraction form of the ratio actually means

Suppose in a class there's <u>girls and boys</u> in the ratio 3 : 4.
This means there's 3/4 as many girls as boys.
So if there were 20 boys, there would be 3/4 × 20 = 15 girls.
You've got to be careful — it <u>doesn't mean</u> 3/4 of the <u>people</u> in the class are girls.

Reducing Ratios to their simplest form

You reduce ratios just like you'd reduce fractions to their simplest form.
For the ratio 15 : 18, both numbers have a <u>factor</u> of 3, so <u>divide them by 3</u>:
That gives 5 : 6. We can't reduce this any further. So the simplest form of 15 : 18 is 5 : 6.

Treat them just like fractions — use your calculator if you can

Now this is really sneaky. If you stick in a fraction using the a^b_c button, your calculator automatically cancels it down when you press =.
So for the ratio 8 : 12, just press 8 a^b_c 12 = , and you'll get the reduced fraction 2/3.
Now you just change it back to ratio form, i.e. <u>2 : 3</u>. Ace.

The More Awkward Cases:

1) The a^b_c button will only accept whole numbers

So IF THE RATIO IS AWKWARD (like "2.4 : 3.6" or "1¼ : 3½") then you must:
<u>MULTIPLY BOTH SIDES</u> by the <u>SAME NUMBER</u> until they are both <u>WHOLE NUMBERS</u>
and then you can use the a^b_c button as before to simplify them down.
e.g. with "1¼ : 3½", × both sides by 4 gives "<u>5 : 14</u>" (Try a^b_c, but it won't cancel further.)

2) If the ratio is MIXED UNITS

then you must <u>CONVERT BOTH SIDES</u> into the <u>SMALLER UNITS</u> using the relevant <u>CONVERSION FACTOR</u> (see P.33), and then carry on as normal.
e.g. "24mm : 7.2cm" (× 7.2cm by 10) ⇒ 24mm : 72mm = <u>1 : 3</u> (using a^b_c)

3) To reduce a ratio to the form 1 : n   (n can be any number at all)

Simply <u>DIVIDE BOTH SIDES BY THE SMALLEST SIDE</u>.
e.g. take "<u>3 : 56</u>" — dividing both sides by 3 gives: <u>1 : 18.7</u> (56÷3) (i.e. 1 : n)
The 1 : n form is often the <u>most useful</u>, since it shows the ratio very clearly.

i wish...

Ratios

Using the Formula Triangle in Ratio Questions

"Mortar is made from sand and cement in the ratio 7:2.
If 9 buckets of sand are used, how much cement is needed?"

This is a fairly common type of Exam question and it's pretty tricky for most people
— but once you start using the formula triangle method, it's all a bit of a breeze really.

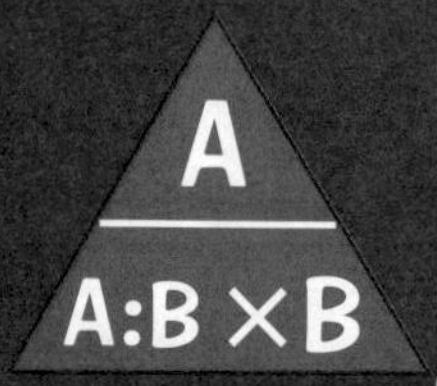

This is the basic **FORMULA TRIANGLE** for **RATIOS**, but **NOTE**:

A
A:B × B

1) **THE RATIO MUST BE THE RIGHT WAY ROUND**,
with the **FIRST NUMBER IN THE RATIO** relating to
the item **ON TOP** in the triangle.

2) You'll always need to **CONVERT THE RATIO** into its
EQUIVALENT FRACTION or Decimal to work out the answer.

The formula triangle for the mortar question is shown below and the trick is to replace
the **RATIO** 7:2 by its **EQUIVALENT FRACTION**: 7/2, or 3.5 as a decimal (7÷2).

So, _covering up cement in the triangle_, gives us "cement = sand / (7:2)"
i.e. "9 / 3.5" = 9 ÷ 3.5 = 2.57 or about _2½ buckets of cement_.

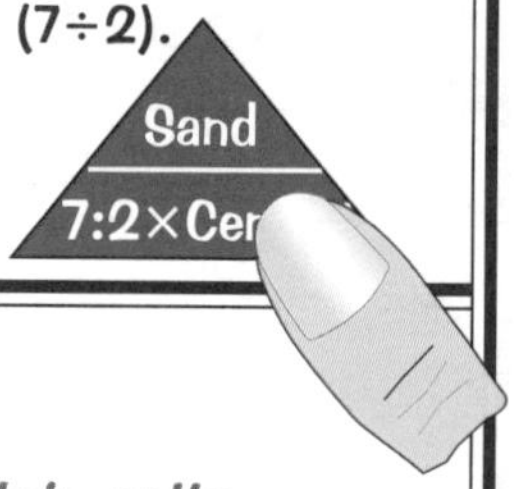

Sand
7:2 × Cer

Proportional _Division_

In a _proportional division question_ a _TOTAL AMOUNT_ is to be _split in a certain ratio_.

For example: _"£9100 is to be split in the ratio 2:4:7. Find the 3 amounts"._

The key word here is **PARTS** — concentrate on "parts" and it all becomes quite painless.

Method

1) **ADD UP THE PARTS**:
The ratio 2:4:7 means there will be a total of 13 _parts_   i.e. 2+4+7 = **13 PARTS**

2) **FIND THE AMOUNT FOR ONE** _"PART"_
Just _divide_ the _total amount_ by the number of _parts_: £9100 ÷ 13 = **£700**   (= 1 PART)

3) **HENCE FIND THE THREE AMOUNTS**:
2 parts = 2×700 = **£1400**,   4 parts = 4×700 = **£2800**,   7 parts = **£4900**

The Acid Test:
LEARN the **RULES** for **SIMPLIFYING**, the
FORMULA TRIANGLE for Ratios (plus 2 points),
and the **3 Steps** for **PROPORTIONAL DIVISION**.

Now _turn over_ and _write down what you've learned_. Try again _until you can do it_.

1) Simplify: a) 25:35   b) 3.4 : 5.1   c) 2¼ : 3¾
2) Porridge and ice-cream are mixed in the ratio 7:4 . How much porridge should go with
10 bowls of ice-cream?   3) Divide £8400 in the ratio 5:3:4

Calculator Buttons

The next few pages are full of lovely calculator tricks to save you a lot of button-bashing.

1) Entering Negative Numbers

Some calculators have a [+/-] button which you press after you've entered the number.
Others just have a minus button [(-)] which you press before entering the number.

So to work out – 5 × – 6 you'd either press... [(-)] [5] [×] [(-)] [6] [=]

or... [5] [+/-] [×] [6] [+/-] [=]

Why can't they all just be the same... (The examples in this book will use the [(-)] button.)

2) The MEMORY BUTTONS [STO], [RCL] (Store and Recall)

(On some calculators the memory buttons are called [Min] (memory in) and [MR] (memory recall).)

Contrary to popular belief, the memory function isn't intended for storing your favourite
phone number, but is in fact a mighty useful feature for keeping a number you've just
calculated, so you can use it again shortly afterwards.

For something like $\dfrac{16}{15+12SIN40}$, you could just work out the bottom line first and stick it

in the memory. Press [15] [+] [12] [SIN] [40] [=] and then [STO] (i.e. [STO] [M] or [STO] [1] or [Min])
to keep the result of the bottom line in the memory.

Then you simply press [16] [÷] [RCL] [=], and the answer is 0.7044.

(Instead of [RCL], you might need to type [RCL] [M] or [RCL] [1] or [MR] on yours.) Once you've practised with the
memory buttons a bit, you'll soon find them very useful. They speed things up no end.

3) BODMAS and the BRACKETS BUTTONS [(] and [)]

One of the biggest problems many people have with their calculator is not realising that it
always works things out in a certain order, which is summarised by the word BODMAS,
which stands for: | Brackets, Other, Division, Multiplication, Addition, Subtraction. |

This becomes of very pressing importance when you want to work out a simple thing like

$\dfrac{23+45}{64\times3}$ — it's no good just pressing [23] [+] [45] [÷] [64] [×] [3] [=] — it will be

completely wrong. The calculator will think you mean $23+\dfrac{45}{64}\times3$ because the

calculator will do the division and multiplication BEFORE it does the addition.

*The secret is to OVERRIDE the automatic BODMAS order of operations using the
BRACKETS BUTTONS. Brackets are the ultimate priority in BODMAS, which means
anything in brackets is worked out before anything else happens to it. So all you have to
do is:*

1) Write a couple of pairs of brackets into the expression:	$\dfrac{(23+45)}{(64\times3)}$
2) Then just type it as it's written:	[(] [23] [+] [45] [)] [÷] [(] [64] [×] [3] [)] [=]

It's not too difficult to decide where to put the brackets in — just put them in pairs around each
group of numbers. It's OK to have brackets within other brackets too, e.g. (4 ÷ (5+2)). As a
rule you can't cause trouble by putting too many brackets in, so long as they always go in pairs.

Calculator Buttons

4) The POWERS BUTTON x^y

The powers button is used for working out powers of numbers <u>quickly</u>.

1) For example to find 7^5, instead of pressing $7 \times 7 \times 7 \times 7 \times 7$ press 7 x^y 5 = [16807]

2) And it's a <u>vital</u> button for working out expressions involving <u>fractional powers</u>.

   e.g. $80^{-3/4}$ ANS: press 80 x^y ((−) 3 $a^{b/c}$ 4) = [0.037383719]

3) The powers button can also be used <u>instead</u> of the square, square root and cube root buttons.

   e.g. $\sqrt{6\tfrac{2}{5}}$ ANS: press (6 $a^{b/c}$ 2 $a^{b/c}$ 5) x^y (1 $a^{b/c}$ 2) = [2.529822128]

     (If you didn't use brackets here, your calculator would probably have given the wrong answer. That's because it doesn't know how much of the expression to apply the X^y to unless you make it clear with brackets. Try it. Get in the habit of using brackets and you'll save yourself a lot of headaches.)

5) Converting Time to Hrs, Mins and Secs with ° ' "

Here's a tricky detail that comes up when you're doing speed, distance and time: <u>converting</u> an answer like <u>2.35 hours into hours and minutes</u>. What it <u>definitely ISN'T</u> is 2 hours and 35 mins — remember your calculator <u>does not</u> work in hours and minutes <u>unless you tell it to</u>, as shown below. You'll need to practise with this button, but you'll be glad you did.

1) <u>To ENTER a time in hours, mins and secs</u>:

   E.g. 5 hrs 34 mins and 23 secs, press 5 °'" 34 °'" 23 °'" = to get [5°34°23] .

2) <u>Converting hours, mins and secs to a decimal time</u>:

   Enter the number in hours, mins and secs as above.

   Then just press °'" and it should convert it to a decimal like this [5.573055556] .

   (Though some older calculators will automatically convert it to decimal when you enter a time in hours, minutes and secs.)

3) <u>To convert a decimal time (as you always get from a formula) into hrs, mins and secs</u>:

   E.g. To convert 2.35 hours into hrs, mins and secs.

   Simply press 2.35 = to enter the decimal, then press °'".

   The display should become [2°21°0] , which means <u>2 hours, 21 mins</u> (and 0 secs).

The Acid test:
LEARN your calculator buttons. Practise until you can answer all of these without having to refer back:

1) Explain what STO and RCL do and give an example of using them.

2) How do you enter a) 6^8 b) 6×10^8 c) $50^{-4/5}$

3) Write down what buttons you would press to work this out in one go: $\dfrac{23.3 + 35.8}{36 \times 26.5}$

4) a) Convert 4.57 hrs into hrs and mins.

   b) Convert 5 hrs 32 mins and 23 secs into decimal hrs.

Conversion Factors

Conversion Factors are a mighty powerful tool for dealing with a wide variety of questions. And what's more the method is real easy. Learn it now. It's ace.

Method
1) Find the <u>Conversion Factor</u>
2) <u>Multiply by it AND divide by it</u>
3) Choose the <u>common sense answer</u>

Four Important Examples

1) *"Convert 2.55 hours into minutes."* — (N.B. This is NOT 2 hrs 55 mins)

1) Conversion factor = <u>60</u> — (simply because 1 hour = <u>60</u> mins)
2) 2.55 hrs × 60 = 153 mins (makes sense)
   2.55 hrs ÷ 60 = 0.0425 mins (ridiculous answer)
3) So plainly the answer is that 2.55 hrs = <u>153 mins</u>

2) *"If £1 = 1.5 Euros, how much is 47.30 Euros in £ and p?"*

1) Obviously, Conversion Factor = <u>1.5</u> (The "exchange rate")
2) 47.30 × 1.5 = £70.95
   47.30 ÷ 1.5 = £31.53
3) Not quite so obvious this time, but if 1.5 Euros = £1, then 47 Euros are LESS than £47, so the answer must be <u>£31.53</u>.

3) *"A map has a scale of 1:20,000. How big in real life is a distance of 3 cm on the map?"*

1) Conversion Factor = 20 000
2) 3cm × 20 000 = 60 000cm (looks OK)
   3cm ÷ 20 000 = 0.00015cm (not good)
3) So <u>60,000 cm</u> is the answer.
   How do we convert to metres? →

To Convert 60,000 cm to m:
1) C.F. = 100 (cm ⟷ m)
2) 60,000 × 100 = 6,000,000 m (hmm)
   60,000 ÷ 100 = <u>600 m</u> (more like it)
3) So answer = <u>600 m</u>

4) Eeek, it's easy to get confused here —
$4m^2$ looks like this not which is $(4m)^2$.

a) *"Convert 4 m^2 into cm^2."*
1) Conversion Factor = 10,000
   (1 m^2 = 100 cm × 100 cm =10,000 cm^2)
2) 4 × 10,000 = 40,000 cm^2 (looks OK)
   4 ÷ 10,000 = 0.0004 cm^2 (silly answer)
3) So <u>40,000 cm^2</u> is the answer.

b) *"Convert 2 m^3 into cm^3."*
1) Conversion Factor = 1,000,000
   (1 m^3 = 100 cm × 100 cm × 100 cm = 1,000,000 cm^3)
2) 2 × 1,000,000 = 2,000,000 cm^3 (looks OK)
   2 ÷ 1,000,000 = 0.000002 cm^3 (silly answer)
3) So <u>2,000,000 cm^3</u> is the answer.

The Acid Test:

LEARN the <u>3 steps</u> of the <u>Conversion Factor</u> method. Then turn over and <u>write them down</u>.

1) Convert 2.3 km into m. 2) Which is more, £174 or 260 Euros? (Exchange rate = 1.5)
3) A map is drawn to a scale of 2 cm = 5 km. A road is 8 km long. How many cm will this be on the map? (Hint, C.F. = 5÷2, i.e. 1 cm = 2.5 km)

Metric and Imperial Units

Make sure you learn all these easy facts:

Metric Units

1) <u>Length</u>   mm, cm, m, km
2) <u>Area</u>   mm², cm², m², km²
3) <u>Volume</u>   mm³, cm³, m³, litres, ml
4) <u>Weight</u>   g, kg, tonnes
5) <u>Speed</u>   km/h, m/s

MEMORISE THESE KEY FACTS:

1cm = 10 mm	1 tonne = 1000 kg
1m = 100 cm	1 litre = 1000 ml
1km = 1000 m	1 litre = 1000 cm³
1kg = 1000 g	1 cm³ = 1 ml

Imperial Units

1) <u>Length</u>   Inches, feet, yards, miles
2) <u>Area</u>   Square inches, square feet, square yards, square miles
3) <u>Volume</u>   Cubic inches, cubic feet, gallons, pints
4) <u>Weight</u>   Ounces, pounds, stones, tons
5) <u>Speed</u>   mph

LEARN THESE TOO!

1 Foot = 12 Inches
1 Yard = 3 Feet
1 Gallon = 8 Pints
1 Stone = 14 Pounds (lbs)
1 Pound = 16 Ounces (oz)

Metric-Imperial Conversions

<u>YOU NEED TO LEARN THESE</u> — they DON'T promise to give you these in the Exam and if they're feeling mean (as they often are), they won't.

APPROXIMATE CONVERSIONS

1 kg = 2¼ lbs	1 gallon = 4.5 litres
1 m = 1 yard (+ 10%)	1 foot = 30 cm
1 litre = 1¾ pints	1 metric <u>tonne</u> = 1 imperial <u>ton</u>
1 inch = 2.5 cm	1 mile = 1.6 km
	or 5 miles = 8 km

Using Metric-Imperial Conversion Factors

1) Convert 45 mm into cm.   CF = 10, so × and ÷ by 10, to get 450cm or <u>4.5cm</u>. (Sensible)
2) Convert 37 inches into cm.   CF = 2.5, so × and ÷ by 2.5, to get <u>92.5cm</u> or 14.8cm.
3) Convert 5.45 litres into pints   CF = 1¾, so × and ÷ by 1.75, to get <u>9.54</u> or 3.11 pints.

The Acid Test:

LEARN the <u>21 Conversion factors</u> in the shaded boxes above. Then <u>turn over and write them down</u>.

1) How many litres is 3½ gallons?   2) Roughly how many yards is 200 m?
3) A rod is 46 inches long. What is this in cm?
4) Petrol costs £2.83 per gallon. What should it cost per litre?
5) A car travels at 65 mph. What is its speed in km/h?

Accuracy and Estimating

Significant Figures (Sig. Fig.)

Significant figures isn't about important people from history — it's about writing numbers down to a certain degree of accuracy. These steps show you how it's done:

1) The <u>1st significant figure</u> of any number is simply
THE FIRST DIGIT WHICH ISN'T A ZERO.

2) The <u>2nd, 3rd, 4th, etc. significant figures</u> follow on immediately after the 1st, REGARDLESS OF WHETHER THEY'RE ZEROS OR NOT ZEROS.

e.g   **0.002309**   **2.03070**

<u>SIG FIGS:</u>   1st 2nd 3rd 4th   1st 2nd 3rd 4th

3) To round to 3 sig. fig. <u>look at the 4th sig.fig.</u> — if it is LESS THAN 5, ROUND the number DOWN. If it's 5 or more ROUND the number UP.

e.g. 0.002309 becomes 0.00231 (to 3 sig. fig.), because 9 is bigger than 5.
e.g. 2.03070 becomes 2.03 (to 3 sig. fig.), because 0 is smaller than 5.

4) After <u>Rounding Off</u> the LAST DIGIT, <u>end ZEROS</u> must be filled in up to, <u>BUT NOT BEYOND, the decimal point</u>.

Examples	to 4 SF	to 3 SF	to 2 SF	to 1 SF
1) 17.0067	17.01	17.0	17	20
2) 0.0045902	0.004590	0.00459	0.0046	0.005
3) 30895.4	30900	30900	31000	30000

Appropriate Accuracy

To decide what is appropriate accuracy, you need only remember these three rules:

1) For fairly <u>casual measurements, 2 SIGNIFICANT FIGURES</u> is most appropriate.

<u>EXAMPLES:</u> Cooking – 250g (2 sig fig) of sugar, not 253g (3 SF), or 300g (1 SF)
Distance of a journey – 450 miles or 25 miles or 3500 miles (All 2 SF)
Area of a garden or floor — 330m² or 15m²

2) For <u>more important or technical things, 3 SIGNIFICANT FIGURES</u> is essential.

<u>EXAMPLES:</u> A technical figure like <u>34.2</u> miles per gallon, rather than 34 mpg.
A length that will be <u>cut to fit</u>, e.g. measure a shelf <u>25.6cm</u> long, not just 26cm.
Any <u>accurate</u> measurement with a ruler: <u>67.5cm</u>, not 70cm or 67.54cm

3) Only for <u>really scientific work</u> would you have <u>more than 3 SIG FIG</u>.

Estimating

This is <u>VERY EASY</u>, so long as you don't <u>over-complicate it</u>.

1) ROUND EVERYTHING OFF to nice easy CONVENIENT NUMBERS
2) Then WORK OUT THE ANSWER using these nice easy numbers — that's it!

In the Exam you'll need to <u>show all the steps</u>, to prove you didn't just use a calculator.

<u>EXAMPLE:</u> Estimate the value of $\frac{127.8+41.9}{56.5\times3.2}$ showing all your working.

Ans: $\frac{127.8+41.9}{56.5\times3.2} \approx \frac{130+40}{60\times3} \approx \frac{170}{180} \approx 1$ (" $\approx$ " means "<u>roughly equal to</u>")

Rounded Off Values

You should be confident about rounding numbers off to a certain number of significant figures. _It gets tricky when they start asking about the maximum and minimum values possible_ for a given level of accuracy in the rounding. This topic is very popular with the Examiners.

1) _Finding the Upper and Lower bounds of a Single Measurement_

The simple rule is this:

> The real value can be as much as HALF THE ROUNDED UNIT above and below the rounded-off value.

_E.g._ _If a length is given as 2.4 m to the nearest 0.1 m, the rounded unit is 0.1 m so the real value could be anything up to 2.4m ± 0.05m giving answers of 2.45m and 2.35m for the upper and lower bounds._

2) _The Maximum and Minimum Possible Values of a Calculation_

When a calculation is done using rounded-off values there will be a <u>DISCREPANCY</u> between the <u>CALCULATED VALUE</u> and the <u>ACTUAL VALUE</u>:

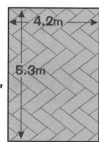

EXAMPLE: A floor is measured as being 5.3 m × 4.2 m to the nearest 10 cm. This gives an area of <u>22.26</u> m², but this is not the actual floor area because

the real values could be anything from <u>5.25 m to 5.35 m</u> and <u>4.15 m to 4.25 m</u>,

∴ Maximum possible floor area = 5.35 × 4.25 = <u>22.7375</u> m²,

∴ Minimum possible floor area = 5.25 × 4.15 = <u>21.7875</u> m².

3) _Maximum Percentage Error_

Having found the two possible extreme values, the one which is <u>FARTHEST</u> from the rounded value will give the maximum percentage error using this familiar formula:

$$\text{Percentage Error} = \frac{\text{Maximum Error}}{\text{Original}} \times 100$$

But watch out — the "original" is the <u>EXTREME</u> value, not the _rounded_ one.

_E.g._ for the above rectangle the max error is _22.7375 – 22.26 = 0.4775_ so the max percentage error is

$$\frac{0.4775}{22.7375} \times 100 = 2.1\%$$

4) _Alas it is not always so simple..._

In many formulas (especially in Exam Questions) it <u>ISN'T</u> the biggest input values that give the maximum result. Consider $z = x + \frac{1}{y}$. The maximum value for z will result from the _maximum_ value for x coupled with the _minimum_ value for y.

So when the question looks more complicated, the _safest method_ is to work out the answer _using all four combinations_ and see which combinations give the maximum and minimum results.

The Acid Test:

<u>LEARN</u> the <u>FOUR POINTS</u> on this page, then <u>turn over</u> and <u>write down</u> the important details for each of them.

1) x and y are measured as 2.32m and 0.45m to the nearest 0.01m. T is given by T = (x − y)/y . Find the maximum possible percentage error in T if the rounded values of x and y are used to calculate it.

Proportion

These questions are all about two amounts that are <u>linked together</u>. If one amount changes, you can work out what the new value is for the other amount.

<u>The Golden Rule</u> is to Work Out One. Once you know the amount of one thing, it's easy to work out any amount.

> Lots of these questions involve money. Usually, you can Work Out One by dividing by the cost. Then multiply to find the new amount.

Direct Proportion

> Direct Proportion — both amounts get bigger together.

Example: A shop assistant earns £7 for 2 hours work.
How much would they earn if they worked for 5 hours?

Answer: Work Out One: £7 ÷ 2 hours = £3.50 pounds for one hour.
And so the pay for 5 hours is 5 × £3.50 = £17.50

> That's what Work Out One means — in this case, work out the pay for one hour.

Food that is sold <u>by weight</u> is another situation that involves proportion.

Example: 3.5 kg of bananas cost £2.80. How much would 5.5kg of bananas cost?

Answer: Work Out One: £2.80 ÷ 3.5 = £0.80 for 1 kg of bananas.
So for 5.5kg you would pay 5.5 × £0.80 = £4.40

Inverse Proportion

> Inverse Proportion — one amount gets bigger when the other gets smaller.

Example: It takes 6 people 5 hours to dig a hole.
How long would it take 10 people?

More people means the job would take less time.

Answer: Work Out One. 6 people × 5 hours = 30 hours work for 1 person.
So 10 people would take 30 ÷ 10 = 3 hours.

Example: 3 friends hire some videos and they pay £2.50 each. If 5 friends got together and hired the same videos, how much each would they pay?

Answer: Work Out One. 3 × £2.50 = £7.50 for one person to hire the videos.
So 5 friends would each pay £7.50 ÷ 5 = £1.50.

Acid Test:

1) What's the golden rule for proportion questions?
2) 2kg of grapes cost £4.60. How much would 3.5 kg of grapes cost?
3) It takes 6 of Santa's elves 4 hours to wrap some presents.
   How long would it take 8 elves?

Direct and Inverse Proportion

Direct Proportion: $y = kx$

BOTH INCREASE TOGETHER

1) The graph of y against x is _a straight line through the origin: $y = kx$._

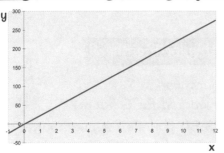

2) In a table of values <u>the MULTIPLIER</u> <u>is the same for X and Y</u>. i.e. if you <u>double</u> one of them, you <u>double</u> the other; if you <u>times one of them by 3</u>, you <u>times the other by 3</u>, etc.

	×3		×2			×4
X	2	6	8	12	14	56
Y	3	9	12	18	21	84
	×3		×2			×4

3) The <u>RATIO</u> $^x/_y$ <u>is the same</u> <u>for all pairs</u> of values, i.e from the table above:

$$\frac{2}{3} = \frac{6}{9} = \frac{8}{12} = \frac{12}{18} = \frac{14}{21} = \frac{56}{84} = 0.6667$$

Inverse Proportion: $y = k/x$

One <u>INCREASES</u> , one <u>DECREASES</u>

The graph of y against x is the well known y=k/x graph:

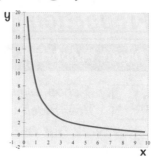

In a table of values the <u>MULTIPLIER</u> for one of them becomes a <u>DIVIDER</u> for the other, i.e. if you <u>double one</u>, you <u>halve the other</u>, if you <u>treble one</u>, you <u>divide the other by three</u>, etc.

	×3		×2			÷4
X	2	6	8	12	40	10
Y	30	10	7.5	5	1.5	6
	÷3		÷2			×4

The <u>PRODUCT</u> XY (X times Y) <u>is the same</u> <u>for all pairs of values</u>,

i.e. in the table above
2 x 30 = 6 x 10 = 8 x 7.5 = 12 x 5
           = 40 x 1.5 = 10 x 6 = <u>60</u>

Inverse Square Variation

You can have all sorts of relationships between x and y, like $y = kx^2$ or $y = k/x^3$ etc. as detailed on P. 39. The most important type is $\underline{y = k/x^2}$ and is called "<u>INVERSE SQUARE</u>" variation. <u>DON'T MIX UP THIS NAME</u> with <u>inverse proportion</u>, which is just $y = k/x$.

The Acid Test:

LEARN the 3 KEY FEATURES for both <u>Direct</u> and <u>Inverse</u> proportion. Then <u>turn over</u> and <u>write them all down</u>.

1) Give examples of 2 real quantities that exhibit a) direct   and b) inverse proportion.
2) Make up your own tables of values which show
          a) DIRECT PROPORTION   b) INVERSE PROPORTION.

Variation

This concerns Exam questions which involve statements like these:

"y is proportional to the square of x"   "t is proportional to the square root of h"
"D varies with the cube of t"   "V is inversely proportional to r cubed"

To deal successfully with things like this <u>you must remember this method</u>:

Method

1) <u>Convert the sentence into a proportionality</u> using the symbol "$\propto$" which means "<u>is proportional to</u>"

2) <u>Replace "$\propto$" with "=k"</u> to make an <u>EQUATION</u>:

The above examples would become:	Proportionality	Equation
"y is proportional to the square of x"	$y \propto x^2$	$y = kx^2$
"t is proportional to the square root of h"	$t \propto \sqrt{h}$	$t = k\sqrt{h}$
"D varies with the cube of t"	$D \propto t^3$	$D = kt^3$
"V is inversely proportional to r cubed"	$V \propto 1/r^3$	$V = k/r^3$

(Once you've got it in the form of an equation with k, <u>the rest is easy</u>)

3) <u>Find a PAIR OF VALUES of x and y</u> somewhere in the question, and <u>SUBSTITUTE</u> them into the equation with the <u>sole purpose of finding k</u>.

4) <u>Put the value of k back into the equation</u> and it's now ready to use.   e.g. $y = 3x^2$

5) <u>INEVITABLY, they'll ask you to find y</u>, having given you a value for x (or vice versa).

Example:

The time taken for a duck to fall down a chimney (it happens!) is inversely proportional to the square of the diameter of the flue. If she took 25 seconds to descend a chimney of diameter 0.3m, how long would it take her to get down one of 0.2m diameter?

(Notice there's no mention of "writing an equation" or "finding k" — it's up to <u>YOU</u> to remember the method for yourself)

<u>ANSWER</u>:
1) Write it as a <u>proportionality</u>, then an <u>equation</u>: $t \propto 1/d^2$ i.e. $t = k/d^2$
2) <u>Sub in the given values</u> for the two variables: $25 = k/0.3^2$
3) Rearrange the equation to <u>find k</u>: $k = 25 \times 0.3^2 = 2.25$
4) Put k <u>back in</u> the formula: $t = 2.25/d^2$
5) <u>Sub in new value</u> for d: $t = 2.25/0.2^2 = \underline{56.25secs}$

The Acid Test:
LEARN the FIVE STEPS of the METHOD plus the <u>four</u> examples. Then <u>turn over and write them all down</u>.

1) The frequency of a pendulum is inversely proportional to the square root of its length. If the pendulum swings with a frequency of 0.5 Hz when the length is 80cm, what frequency will it have with a length of 50cm, and what length will give a frequency of 0.7 Hz?

Typical Graph Questions

Graphs are really good and everybody likes them a lot more than they let on, I'm sure.

Filling in The Table of Values

A typical question would say "Complete the table of values for the equation $y = x^2 - 4x + 3$."

x	-2	-1	0	1	2	3	4	5	6
y				0			3		15

The rest of the question hinges on this table of values and one silly mistake here could cost you lots of marks — <u>YOU NEED TO MAKE SURE YOU GET THE NUMBERS RIGHT</u>:

1) First, <u>MAKE SURE YOU CAN REPRODUCE ANY VALUES THAT ARE ALREADY DONE</u>.

2) Once you've checked out your method, work out the other values <u>AT LEAST TWICE</u>.

3) Try to spot any <u>SYMMETRY or PATTERN</u> in the values, and check any that seem out of place.

You should be able to work out each value in one go on the calculator, but if things aren't working out you'll have to do a <u>SAFER METHOD</u>. For each value in the table you might be wise to write this out:

$$\underline{x=4} \qquad \begin{aligned} y &= x^2 - 4x + 3 \\ &= 4^2 - 4\times4 + 3 \\ &= 16 - 16 + 3 = 3 \end{aligned}$$

<u>It's worth it, if it means you get it RIGHT rather than WRONG!</u>

Plotting the Points and Drawing the Curve

Here again there are <u>easy marks to be won and lost</u>. All these points matter:

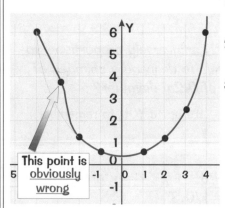

This point is <u>obviously wrong</u>

1) <u>Get the axes the right way round</u>: The values from the <u>FIRST row or column</u> are ALWAYS plotted <u>on the X-axis</u>.

2) Plot the points CAREFULLY, and don't muddle up the x and y values.

3) The points will ALWAYS form a <u>DEAD STRAIGHT LINE</u> or a <u>COMPLETELY SMOOTH CURVE</u>. NEVER EVER let one <u>point drag your line off</u> in some ridiculous direction. If one point seems out of place, <u>check the value in the table</u> and then the position where you've plotted it. When a graph is generated from an equation, <u>you never get spikes or lumps</u> — only MISTAKES.

4) A graph from an <u>ALGEBRA EQUATION</u> must always be a <u>SMOOTH CURVE</u> (or a dead straight line). You only use short straight-line sections to join points in "<u>Data Handling</u>".

The Acid Test:
LEARN the <u>3 Rules for tables of values</u> and the <u>4 points for drawing graphs</u>, then turn over and <u>write them down</u>.

1) <u>Complete the table of values</u> at the top of the page (applying the three rules of course).
2) Then <u>draw the graph</u>, taking note of the four points.
3) Using your graph, <u>find the value of y when x is 4.2</u>, and <u>the values of x when y=12</u>.

Plotting Straight-Line Graphs

Some people wouldn't know a straight-line equation if it ran up and bit them, but they're pretty easy to spot really — they just have <u>two letters</u> and <u>a few numbers</u>, but <u>nothing fancy</u> like squared or cubed, as shown on page 61.

Anyway, in the Exam you'll be expected to be able to draw the graphs of straight-line equations. "y = mx + c" is the hard way of doing it (see P.63), but here's <u>TWO NICE EASY WAYS</u> of doing it:

1) The "Table of 3 values" method

You can <u>EASILY</u> draw the graph of <u>ANY EQUATION</u> using this <u>EASY</u> method:

> 1) Choose <u>3 VALUES OF X</u> and <u>draw up a wee table</u>,
> 2) <u>WORK OUT THE Y-VALUES</u>,
> 3) <u>PLOT THE COORDINATES</u>, and <u>DRAW THE LINE</u>.

If it's a *straight-line equation*, the 3 points will be in a *dead straight line* with each other, which is <u>the usual check you do when you've drawn it</u> — *if they aren't*, then it could be a <u>curve</u> and you'll need to do *more values in your table* to find out what on earth's going on. (See P.40)

Example:

"Draw the graph of Y = 2X – 3"

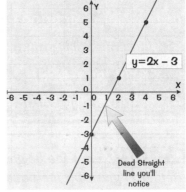

1) <u>DRAW UP A TABLE</u> with some *suitable* values of X. Choosing X = 0, 2, 4 is usually cool enough.   i.e.

X	0	2	4
Y			

2) <u>FIND THE Y-VALUES</u> by putting each x-value into the equation:

X	0	2	4
Y	-3	1	5

(e.g. When <u>X = 4</u>, $y = 2X - 3 = 2 \times 4 - 3 = 5$)

3) <u>PLOT THE POINTS</u> and <u>DRAW THE LINE</u>.

2) The "X = 0", "Y = 0" Method

This is especially good for equations of the form: "ax + by = c"

> 1) <u>Set x=0</u> in the equation and <u>FIND Y</u> — this is where it <u>CROSSES THE Y-AXIS</u>.
>
> 2) <u>Set y=0</u> in the equation and <u>FIND X</u> — this is where it <u>CROSSES THE X-AXIS</u>.
>
> 3) <u>Plot these two points</u> and <u>join them up with a straight line</u> — *and just hope it should be a straight line, since with only 2 points you can't really tell, can you!*

Example:

"Draw the graph of 5x + 3y = 15"

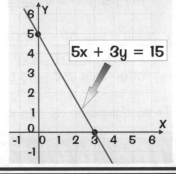

1) Putting <u>x = 0</u> gives "3y = 15" $\Rightarrow$ <u>y = 5</u>

2) Putting <u>y = 0</u> gives "5x = 15" $\Rightarrow$ <u>x = 3</u>

3) So plot y = 5 on the y-axis and x = 3 on the x-axis and join them up with a straight line:

Only doing 2 points is risky unless you're sure the equation is definitely a straight line — but then that's the big thrill of living life on the edge, isn't it.

The Acid Test:

<u>LEARN</u> the details of these <u>TWO EASY METHODS</u> then <u>turn over and write down all you know.</u>

1) Draw these graphs using <u>both</u> methods   a) y = 4 + x   b) 4y + 3x = 12   c) y = 6 – 2x

Solving Equations Using Graphs

This is an easy type of graph question — you just _draw a graph of the equation_ and then _draw lines from one axis or the other to meet it_. Really you should be _half EXPECTING_ that to happen, because that's _the most simple and obvious thing to do_ with any graph.

The Answers _are where the_ X- _or_ Y-value _Hits the_ Graph

The typical question will have a _nasty-looking equation_ a bit like this: $y = 2x^2 - 3$ and a _graph_ already drawn for you.

Then they'll ask you something like this:
"_From the graph, find the values of x which make y = 4._"

This is how you do it:

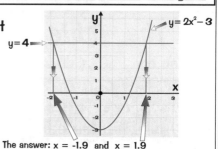

The answer: x = -1.9 and x = 1.9

The Easy Peasy _Four-Step Method_

1) Draw (or finish off) the _GRAPH_ from a _TABLE OF VALUES_.   (See P.40)

2) Draw a line _ACROSS_ (or _UP_) from the _Y-AXIS_ (or _X-AXIS_) at the value _GIVEN_.

3) Where it _crosses the graph_, draw a line (or lines) _DOWN_ (or _ACROSS_) to the _X-AXIS_ (or _Y-AXIS_).

4) _READ OFF_ the _VALUES_ from the _X-AXIS_ (or _Y-AXIS_) — and they're the _ANSWERS_.

Example:
The height, h, gained by a small piece of mouldy cheese fired from a catapult is given by the equation _$h = 25t - 5t^2$_. Using a _graphical method_ find a) the times at which the mouldy cheese is at a height of 25m and   b) its height after 2½ secs.

ANSWER:

1) First _draw the graph from the equation_, doing your own _table of values_ if necessary.

time	0	1	2	3	4	5
height	0	20	30	30	20	0

2) Draw the graph. Note the CURVED PEAK. DON'T EVER join the two points near the peak with a _ridiculous straight line_.

Eeek!

3) _Draw a line UP or ACROSS_ from the axis (using the given value), _hit the curve_ and _go ACROSS or DOWN_ to the other axis and _read off the value_. Easy as that.

height h (metres)

The answers

time t (seconds)

From the graph we can see the answers to this question are   a) 1.4s and 3.6s   b) 31m

The Acid Test:
LEARN THE IMPORTANT DETAILS on this page, then _turn over and write them all down_. Keep trying till you can.

1) Using the above graph for $h = 25t - 5t^2$, find the values of t which give h = 15m.
2) Do a table of values and a graph for $y = x^2 + 2x - 3$.
   a) Find the values of x when y = –2.   b) Find the values of x which give y=0.

Also in module 5:

Simultaneous Equations and Graphs

When you have _two graphs_ which represent _two separate equations_, there are two ways the question can present it: _TWO SIMULTANEOUS EQUATIONS_ or a _single MERGED EQUATION_. In either case _THE SOLUTIONS_ will simply be _WHERE THE TWO GRAPHS CROSS_ (fairly obviously).

Also in module 5:

1) Two Graphs and Two Separate Equations

Example "Draw the graphs for "Y = 2X + 3" and "Y = 6 – 4X" and then use your graphs to solve them."

1) <u>TABLE OF 3 VALUES</u> (see P.40)
   for both equations:

X	0	2	– 2
Y	3	7	– 1

X	0	2	3
Y	6	– 2	– 6

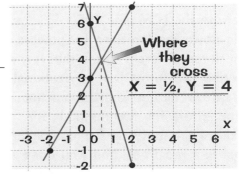

Where they cross
X = ½, Y = 4

2) <u>DRAW THE GRAPHS:</u>

3) <u>WHERE THEY CROSS:</u> x = ½, y = 4.
   And that's the answer!

   | x = ½ and y = 4 |

2) Two Graphs but Just ONE Equation, or so it seems...

Example "Using the graphs shown for Y = 4 + ½X and Y = 6 – X²/3, _solve the equation:_ X²/3 + ½X – 2 = 0."

<u>ANSWER:</u> _Learn_ these important steps:

1) _Equating the equations_ of the two graphs gives this:
   $6 – X^2/3 = 4 + ½X$ (a sort of _"merged"_ equation)

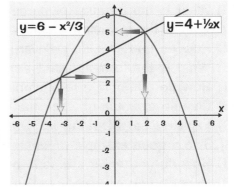

$y = 6 – x^2/3$ $y = 4 + ½x$

2) Now bring it all onto _one side_ and you end up with:
   $X^2/3 + ½X – 2 = 0$ (the equation in the question!)

3) Hence the _solutions_ to that equation are where the two initial equations ($Y = 4 + ½X$ and $Y = 6 – X^2/3$) are _equal_ — i.e. where their _graphs cross_, which as the graph shows is at: <u>x = 1.8</u> or <u>x = -3.3</u>.

4) The _same_ question _could_ have been asked differently: "Using the graphs shown, _solve_ the two _simultaneous equations:_ $Y = 4 + ½X$ and $Y = 6 – X^2/3$"
   <u>ANSWER:</u> From where the graphs cross: <u>X=1.8, Y=4.9</u>, or <u>X=-3.3, Y=2.3</u>.

Even if you're not sure, you should <u>GUESS</u> the answers to be the _points of intersection_ and just write them down.   Also note that for _simultaneous equations_ you give _BOTH_ the X-values AND Y-values whilst for the _"merged equation"_ you _just give the X-values_. That's because the merged equation doesn't have any _Y_ in it to start with (even though the two equations it's derived from do) — tricky details, but you have to learn them.

The Acid Test:

1) Use graphs to find the solutions to these pairs of equations:
   a) Y = 4x – 4 and Y = 6 – X   b) Y = 2x   and Y = 6 – 2x
2) Draw the graphs of y = 2x² – 4 and y = 2 – x and hence solve 2x² + x = 6.

Revision Summary for Module Three

These questions may seem difficult, _but they are the very best revision you can do_. They follow the sequence of pages in Module Three, so you can easily look up anything you don't know.

Keep learning these basic facts until you know them

1) What are square numbers and cube numbers?
2) How do you estimate a square root?
3) What is the method for deciding if a number is prime?
4) What are factors?
5) What are the LCM and HCF?
6) Write down the ten rules for powers and roots.
7) Name three different forms that a rational number can take, and give examples.
8) Describe two forms that an irrational number can take, with examples.
9) Write down all you know about manipulating surds.
10) Demonstrate the two methods for turning recurring decimals into fractions.
11) What are the methods for multiplying and dividing decimals?
12) What is a reciprocal and why does zero have no reciprocal?
13) What is the format of any number expressed in standard form?
14) Which is the standard form button? What would you press to enter 6×10^8?
15) Describe the method for multiplying or dividing numbers written in standard form.
16) What is a term? Give an example.
17) Describe the steps for simplifying an expression involving several terms.
18) Describe the five rules for doing fractions by hand.
19) Do your own examples to illustrate each of the three types of percentage question.
20) What is the formula for percentage change? Give two examples of its use.
21) What is the formula for compound growth and decay? Give 3 examples of its use.
22) How do you simplify awkward ratios, e.g. 3.25 : 4.5?
23) What is the formula triangle method for ratios?
24) How do you split a total amount in a certain ratio?
25) Give an example of when the memory buttons on your calculator should be used.
26) Explain what BODMAS is. Does your calculator know about it?
27) Give a good example of when the brackets buttons should be used.
28) How do you enter a time in hours, minutes and seconds on your calculator?
29) How do you convert hours, minutes and seconds to decimal time and back again?
30) What are the three steps for using conversion factors? Give three examples.
31) Give 8 metric, 5 imperial and 8 metric-to-imperial conversions.
32) What's the method for writing a number to three significant figures?
33) Give three rules for deciding on appropriate accuracy.
34) How do you find the maximum possible percentage error?
35) Give an example of direct proportion and an example of inverse proportion.
36) What is the difference between inverse proportion and inverse square proportion?
37) What are the five steps for dealing with questions on variation?
38) What is the process for drawing a graph from an equation?
39) What are the four steps for solving equations using graphs?
40) What is meant by a "merged equation", and how do you solve it using graphs?

Number Patterns

This is an easy topic, but make sure you know **ALL EIGHT** types of sequence, not just the first few. The *main secret* is to *write the differences in the gaps* between each pair of numbers. That way you can usually see what's happening, whichever type it is.

1) "COMMON DIFFERENCE" Type — dead easy

e.g.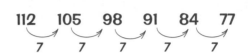

2) "INCREASING DIFFERENCE" Type

Here the differences <u>increase by the</u> <u>same amount</u> each time:

e.g.

3) "DECREASING DIFFERENCE" Type

Here the differences <u>decrease by</u> the <u>same amount</u> each time:

e.g.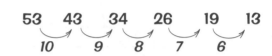

4) "MULTIPLYING FACTOR" Type

This type has a common **MULTIPLIER** linking each pair of numbers:

e.g.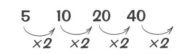

5) "DIVIDING FACTOR" Type

This type has a common **DIVIDER** linking each pair of numbers:

e.g.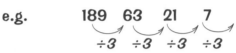

6) "ADDING PREVIOUS TERMS" Type

Add the *first two terms* to get the *3rd*, then add the *2nd and 3rd* to get the *4th*, etc.

e.g.   1   1   2   3   5   8   13   21

　　　　　　1+1 1+2 2+3 3+5 5+8 8+13 13+21

7) "TRIANGLE NUMBERS"

To remember the triangle numbers you have to picture in your mind this *increasing pattern of triangles*, where each new row has *one more blob* than the previous row.

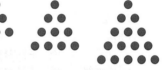

| 1 | 3 | 6 | 10 | 15 | 21 | 28 | 36 | 45 | 55... |

　　2　3　4　5　6　7　8　9　10　11　12

It's definitely worth learning this simple *pattern of differences*, as well as the formula for the *nth term* (see P.46) which is:

$$\text{nth term} = \tfrac{1}{2}\, n\, (n + 1)$$

8) "POWERS"

Powers are "numbers *multiplied by themselves* so many times".

"Two to the power three" $= 2^3 = 2 \times 2 \times 2 = 8$

Here's the first few *POWERS OF 2*:   ... and the first *POWERS OF 10* (even easier):

| 2 | 4 | 8 | 16 | 32... |

$2^1=2$　$2^2=4$　$2^3=8$　$2^4=16$　etc...

| 10 | 100 | 1000 | 10 000 | 100 000... |

$10^1=10$　$10^2=100$　$10^3=1000$　etc...

The Acid Test:

LEARN the 8 types of number pattern.
Then cover the page and answer these:

Find the next two terms in these sequences:
1) 2,6,18,54...   2) 1,3,4,7,11....   3) 3,5,8,12,17,...   4) 128,64,32,...

Finding the nth Term

"The nth term" is a formula with "n" in it which gives you every term in a sequence when you put different values for n in. There are two different types of sequence (for "nth term" questions) which have to be done in different ways:

Common Difference Type: "dn + (a – d)"

For any sequence such as 3, 7, 11, 15, where there is a COMMON DIFFERENCE
                                    4   4   4

you can always find "the nth term" using the FORMULA: **nth term = dn + (a–d)**
Don't forget:

> 1) "a" is simply the value of THE FIRST TERM in the sequence.
> 2) "d" is simply the value of THE COMMON DIFFERENCE between the terms.
> 3) To get the *nth term*, you just *find the values of "a" and "d" from the sequence and stick them in the formula*.
>   *You don't replace n though — that wants to stay as n*
> 4) — of course YOU HAVE TO LEARN THE FORMULA, but life is like that.

Example: *"Find the nth term of this sequence: 5,   8,   11,   14 ...."*

ANSWER: 1) The formula is dn + (a – d)
2) The first term is 5, so a = 5   The common difference is 3 so d = 3
3) Putting these in the formula gives: 3n + (5–3)
                                                       so the nth term = 3n + 2

Changing Difference Type:
"a + (n–1)d + ½(n–1)(n–2)C"

If the number sequence is one where the difference between the terms is *increasing or decreasing* then it gets a whole lot more complicated (as you'll have spotted from the above formula — which you'll have to *learn!*). This time there are THREE letters you have to fill in:

"a" is the FIRST TERM,
"d" is the FIRST DIFFERENCE (between the first two numbers),
"C" is the CHANGE BETWEEN ONE DIFFERENCE AND THE NEXT.

Example: *"Find the nth term of this sequence: 2, 5, 9, 14 ...."*
                                                                          3   4   5
ANSWER: 1) The formula is "a + (n–1)d + ½(n–1)(n–2)C"
2) The *first term* is 2, so a = 2   The *first difference* is 3 so d = 3
3) The *differences increase* by 1 each time so C = +1
Putting these in the formula gives: "2 + (n–1)3 + ½(n–1)(n–2)×1"
    Which becomes: 2 + 3n – 3 + ½n² – 1½n + 1
    Which simplifies to: ½n² + 1½n = ½n(n+3)   so the *nth term = ½n(n+3)*.

The Acid Test: LEARN the definition of the nth term and PRACTISE USING THE FORMULAS.

1) Find the nth term of the following sequences:
a) 4, 7, 10, 13.... b) 3, 8, 13, 18,..... c) 1, 3, 6, 10, 15,..... d) 3, 4, 7, 12,...

More Algebra

D.O.T.S. — The Difference of Two Squares:

The "difference of two squares" (D.O.T.S. for short) is where you have "one thing squared" minus "another thing squared".

$$a^2 - b^2 = (a + b)(a - b)$$

This is an identity. It works for ALL values of a and b.

If you multiply out the factorised form you can see it's the same as the "difference of two squares":

$$(a + b)(a - b) = a^2 - \cancel{ba} + \cancel{ab} - b^2 \quad \text{"ba" cancels out "− ab"}$$
$$= a^2 - b^2$$

In the Exam you'll more than likely be asked to factorise a D.O.T.S. expression (i.e. put it into two brackets as above).

Too many people have more trouble than they should with this, probably because they don't make enough effort to learn it as a separate item in its own right. Best learn it now, eh, before it's too late. Make sure you **LEARN** these three important examples:

1) Factorise $9P^2 - 16Q^2$.   Answer: $9P^2 - 16Q^2 = \underline{(3P + 4Q)(3P - 4Q)}$

2) Factorise $1 - T^4$.   Answer: $1 - T^4 = \underline{(1 + T^2)(1 - T^2)}$

3) Factorise $K^2 - 25H^2$.   Answer: $K^2 - 25H^2 = \underline{(K + 5H)(K - 5H)}$

Multiplying out Brackets

1) The thing <u>outside</u> the brackets <u>multiplies each separate term inside the brackets</u>.
2) When letters are multiplied together, they are just written next to each other, e.g. pq.
3) Remember, $R \times R = R^2$ and TY^2 means $T \times Y \times Y$, whilst $(TY)^2$ means $T \times T \times Y \times Y$.
4) Remember <u>a minus outside the bracket REVERSES ALL THE SIGNS when you multiply</u>.

1) $3(2x + 5) = \underline{6x + 15}$ 2) $4p(3r - 2t) = \underline{12pr - 8pt}$

3) $-4(3p^2 - 7q^3) = -12p^2 + 28q^3$ (note both signs have been reversed)

5) DOUBLE BRACKETS — you get <u>4 terms</u>, and usually 2 of them combine to leave <u>3 terms</u>.

$$(2P - 4)(3P + 1) = (2P \times 3P) + (2P \times 1) + (-4 \times 3P) + (-4 \times 1)$$
$$= 6P^2 + 2P - 12P - 4$$
$$= \underline{6P^2 - 10P - 4} \quad \text{(these 2 combine together)}$$

6) SQUARED BRACKETS — ALWAYS write these out as TWO BRACKETS:

E.g. $(3d + 5)^2$ should be written out as $(3d + 5)(3d + 5)$ and then work them out as above.
YOU SHOULD ALWAYS GET <u>FOUR</u> TERMS from a pair of brackets.
The usual <u>WRONG ANSWER</u> is $(3d + 5)^2 = 9d^2 + 25$ (eeek)
It should be: $(3d + 5)^2 = (3d + 5)(3d + 5) = 9d^2 + 15d + 15d + 25 = \underline{9d^2 + 30d + 25}$

More Algebra

Factorising — putting brackets in.

This is the exact reverse of multiplying out brackets. Here's the method to follow:

1) Take out the biggest number that goes into all the terms.
2) Take each letter in turn and take out the highest power (e.g. x, x^2 etc) that will go into EVERY term.
3) Open the brackets and fill in all the bits needed to reproduce each term.

EXAMPLE: *"Factorise $15x^4y + 20x^2y^3z - 35x^3yz^2$"*

Answer: $5x^2y(3x^2 + 4y^2z - 7xz^2)$

Biggest number that'll divide into 15, 20 and 35.

Highest powers of x and y that will go into all three terms.

z was not in ALL terms so it can't come out as a common factor.

REMEMBER:
1) The bits *taken out* and put at the front are the *common factors*.
2) The bits *inside the brackets* are *what's needed to get back to the original terms* if you multiplied the brackets out again.

Algebraic Fractions

The basic rules are exactly the same as for ordinary fractions (see P.26), and you should definitely be aware of the close similarity.

1) Multiplying (easy)

Multiply top and bottom separately and cancel if possible:

$$\text{e.g.} \quad \frac{st}{10w^3} \times \frac{35s^2tw}{6} = \frac{35s^3t^2w}{60w^3} = \frac{7s^3t^2}{12w^2}$$

2) Dividing (easy)

Turn the second one upside down, then multiply and cancel if possible:

$$\text{e.g.} \quad \frac{12}{p+4} \div \frac{4(p-3)}{3(p+4)} = \frac{\cancel{12}^{\,3}}{\cancel{p+4}} \times \frac{3\cancel{(p+4)}}{\cancel{4}(p-3)} = \frac{9}{p-3}$$

3) Adding/subtracting (not so easy)

Always get a common denominator i.e. same bottom line (by cross-multiplying) and then ADD TOP LINES ONLY:

$$\frac{t-2p}{3t-p} - \frac{1}{3} = \frac{3(t-2p)}{3(3t-p)} - \frac{1(3t-p)}{3(3t-p)} = \frac{3t-6p-3t+p}{3(3t-p)} = \frac{-5p}{3(3t-p)}$$

The Acid Test: LEARN THE DETAILS of all the sections on pages 47 and 48. Then turn over and write down what you've learned.

1) Factorise: a) $X^2 - 16Y^2$ b) $49 - 81P^2Q^2$

2) Expand $2pq(3p - 4q^2)$

3) Expand $(2g + 5)(4g - 2)$

4) Factorise $14x^2y^3 + 21xy^2 - 35x^3y^4$

5) Simplify $\dfrac{5abc^3}{18de} \div \dfrac{15abd^2}{9ce}$

6) Simplify $\dfrac{3}{5} + \dfrac{5g}{3g - 4}$

Speed and Density Formulas

Formula triangles are EXTREMELY POTENT TOOLS for dealing with common formulas.
They're VERY EASY, so make sure you know how to use them.

Speed = Distance ÷ Time

Questions on speed are always coming up in exams, and they never give you the formula.
Either you learn it beforehand or you wave goodbye to several easy marks.

It makes life easier if you learn the speed formula as this FORMULA TRIANGLE.➤ **D / S × T**

How Do You Use Formula Triangles?

1) COVER UP the thing you want to find and just WRITE DOWN what is left showing.

2) Now PUT IN THE VALUES for the other two things and WORK IT OUT.

EXAMPLE: "A car travels 90 miles at 36 miles per hour. How long does it take?"
ANSWER: We want to find the time, so cover up T in the triangle which leaves D/S,
so T = D/S = Distance ÷ speed = 90 ÷ 36 = 2.5 hours

Of course you have to remember the order of the letters in
the triangle (SDT), and we have the word SoDiT to help you.

So if it's a question on speed, distance and time just say: **SOD IT.**

Density is Another Important Example:

The standard formula for density is:

DENSITY = MASS ÷ VOLUME

But the best method of learning it by far
is to remember this FORMULA TRIANGLE.

If you remember it as D^{M}V or DiMoV (the Russian Agent) you won't go far wrong.

EXAMPLE: "Find the volume of an object with a mass of 40 g and a density of 6.4 g/cm³."
ANSWER:
To find the volume, cover up V. This leaves M/D, so V = M ÷ D = 40 ÷ 6.4 = 6.25 cm³.

> IF YOU LEARN THE FORMULA TRIANGLES, YOU WILL FIND
> QUESTIONS ON SPEED AND DENSITY VERY EASY.

The Acid Test:

LEARN the Formula Triangles for density and speed.
Then turn over and write them from memory.

1) First see page 32 to remind yourself and then find the time taken, in hours, mins and
secs, for a purple-nosed buffalo walking at 3.2 km/h to cover 5.2 km.
2) A metal object has a volume of 45 cm³ and a mass of 743 g. What is its density?
3) Another piece of the same metal has a volume of 36.5 cm³. What is its mass?

Solving Equations

Solving Equations means finding the value of x from something like: $3x + 5 = 4 - 5x$. The same sequence of steps applies each time.

To illustrate the sequence of steps we'll use this equation:

$$\sqrt{2 - \frac{x+4}{2x+5}} = 3$$

An *expression* is any collection of numbers or symbols, e.g. 2xy.

An *equation* has two expressions, linked with an *equals sign*, e.g. 2xy = 5y + 6.

The Six Steps Applied to Equations

1) Get rid of any square root signs by <u>squaring both sides</u>:

$$2 - \frac{x+4}{2x+5} = 9$$

2) Get everything off the bottom by <u>cross-multiplying up to EVERY OTHER TERM</u>:

$$2 - \frac{x+4}{2x+5} = 9 \quad \Rightarrow \quad 2(2x+5) - (x+4) = 9(2x+5)$$

3) <u>Multiply out</u> any brackets:

$$4x + 10 - x - 4 = 18x + 45$$

4) Collect all <u>subject terms</u> on one side of the "=" and all <u>non-subject terms</u> on the other. <u>Remember to reverse the +/− sign of any term that crosses the "="</u>

+18x moves across the "=" and becomes -18x
+10 moves across the "=" and becomes -10
-4 moves across the "=" and becomes +4

$$4x - x - 18x = 45 - 10 + 4$$

5) <u>Combine like terms</u> on each side of the equation, and reduce it to the form "<u>Ax = B</u>", where A and B are just numbers:

$$-15x = 39$$
("Ax = B": A = -15, B = 39, x is the subject)

6) Finally <u>slide the A underneath the B</u> to give "X = B/A", divide, and that's your answer.

$$x = \frac{39}{-15} = -2.6$$

So <u>x = -2.6</u>

The Seventh Step (if You Need It)

If the term you're trying to find is squared, don't panic.

Follow steps 1) to 6) like normal, but solve it for x^2 instead of x: $\quad x^2 = 9$

$$x = \pm 3$$

7) <u>Take the square root</u> of both sides and stick a ± sign in front of the number:

Don't forget the ± sign...
(P.19 if you don't know what I mean).

The Acid Test:

1) Solve these equations: a) $5(x + 2) = 8 + 4(5 - x)$ b) $\frac{4}{x+3} = \frac{6}{4-x}$ c) $x^2 - 21 = 5(3 - x^2)$

Rearranging Formulas

Rearranging Formulas means making one letter the subject, e.g. getting "y= " from something like $2x + z = 3(y + 2p)$.

Generally speaking "solving equations" is easier, but don't forget:

1) EXACTLY THE SAME METHOD APPLIES TO BOTH FORMULAS AND EQUATIONS.
2) THE SAME SEQUENCE OF STEPS APPLIES EVERY TIME.

We'll illustrate this by making "y" the subject of this formula: $M = \sqrt{2K - \dfrac{K^2}{2y+1}}$

The Six Steps Applied to Formulas

1) Get rid of any square root signs by <u>squaring both sides</u>: $\quad M^2 = 2K - \dfrac{K^2}{2y+1}$

2) Get everything off the bottom by <u>cross-multiplying up to EVERY OTHER TERM</u>:

$$M^2 = 2K - \frac{K^2}{2y+1} \Rightarrow M^2(2y+1) = 2K(2y+1) - K^2$$

3) <u>Multiply out</u> any brackets: $\quad 2yM^2 + M^2 = 4Ky + 2K - K^2$

4) Collect all <u>subject terms</u> on one side of the "=" and all <u>non-subject terms</u> on the other. <u>Remember to reverse the +/– sign of any term that crosses the "="</u>

+4Ky moves across the "=" and becomes –4Ky
+M² moves across the "=" and becomes –M²

$$2yM^2 - 4Ky \;\; = \;\; -M^2 + 2K - K^2$$

(+/- +/-)

5) <u>Combine like terms</u> on each side of the formula, and reduce it to the form "<u>Ax = B</u>", where A and B are just bunches of letters which DON'T include the subject (y). Note that the LHS has to be <u>FACTORISED</u>:

$$(2M^2 - 4K)y = 2K - K^2 - M^2$$

("Ax = B" i.e. $A = (2M^2 - 4K)$, $B = 2K - K^2 - M^2$,   y is the subject)

6) Finally <u>slide the A underneath the B</u> to give "$X = \dfrac{B}{A}$".
(cancel if possible) and that's your answer.   So $y = \dfrac{2K - K^2 - M^2}{(2M^2 - 4K)}$

The Seventh Step (if You Need It)

$$M = \sqrt{2K - \frac{K^2}{2y^2+1}}$$

If the term you're trying to make the subject of the equation is squared, this is what you do:

Follow steps 1) to 6), $y^2 = \dfrac{2K - K^2 - M^2}{(2M^2 - 4K)}$ and then...

(I've skipped steps 1) - 6) because they're exactly the same as the first example — but with y^2 instead of y.)

7) <u>Take the square root</u> of both sides and stick a $\pm$ sign in front of the expression on the right: $y = \pm\sqrt{\dfrac{2K - K^2 - M^2}{(2M^2 - 4K)}}$

Remember — square roots can be +ve or –ve. See P.19.

The Acid Test:

LEARN the <u>7 STEPS</u> for <u>solving equations</u> and <u>rearranging formulas</u>. Turn over and write them down.

1) Rearrange "$F = \frac{9}{5}C + 32$" from "F= ", to "C= " and then back the other way.
2) Make p the subject of these: a) $\dfrac{p}{p+y} = 4$ b) $\dfrac{1}{p} = \dfrac{1}{q} + \dfrac{1}{r}$ c) $\dfrac{1}{p^2} = \dfrac{1}{q} + \dfrac{1}{r}$

Inequalities

Inequalities aren't half as difficult as they look. The inequality symbols are confusing at first, but most of the algebra for them is identical to ordinary equations.

THE INEQUALITY SYMBOLS:

> means "<u>Greater than</u>" $\geqslant$ means "<u>Greater than or equal to</u>"

< means "<u>Less than</u>" $\leqslant$ means "<u>Less than or equal to</u>"

<u>REMEMBER</u>, the one at the <u>BIG</u> end is <u>BIGGEST</u>.

so $X > 4$ and $4 < X$ both mean: "<u>X is greater than 4</u>".

Algebra With Inequalities

$5X < X + 2$
$5X = X + 2$

The thing to remember here is that <u>inequalities are just like regular equations</u> in the sense that <u>all the normal rules of algebra apply</u> (See P.47-48) — WITH ONE BIG EXCEPTION:

Whenever you MULTIPLY OR DIVIDE BY A <u>NEGATIVE NUMBER</u>, you must <u>REVERSE THE INEQUALITY SIGN</u>.

Three Important Examples

1) Solve $5X < 6X + 2$

The equivalent equation is $5X = 6X + 2$, which is easy — and so is the inequality:

First subtract 6X: $5X - 6X < 2$ which gives $-X < 2$

Then divide both sides by –1: $\underline{X > -2}$ (i.e. X is greater than –2)

(NOTE: The < has flipped around into a >, because we divided by a –ve number)

This answer, $\underline{X > -2}$, can be displayed on a number line like this:

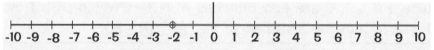

2) Find all integer values of x where $-4 \leqslant x < 1$ *(Integers are positive or negative whole numbers.)*

This type of expression is <u>very common</u> — <u>YOU MUST LEARN TO READ THEM IN THIS WAY</u>:

" X is between –4 and +1, possibly equal to –4 but never equal to +1 ".

(Obviously the answers are <u>–4, –3, –2, –1, 0</u> (but not 1).)

3) Find the range of values of X where $X^2 \leqslant 25$

The trick here is: <u>DON'T FORGET THE NEGATIVE VALUES</u>.

Square-rooting both sides gives $X \leqslant 5$. However, this is <u>ONLY HALF THE STORY</u>, because $-5 \leqslant X$ is also true. There is little alternative but to simply LEARN this:

1) $X^2 \leqslant 25$ gives the solution $-5 \leqslant X \leqslant 5$,
(X is between –5 and 5, possibly equal to either.)

2) $X^2 \geqslant 36$ gives the solution: $X \leqslant -6$ or $6 \leqslant X$
(X is "less than or equal to –6" or "greater than or equal to +6".)

The Acid Test:

<u>LEARN</u> all of this page including the Three important Examples, then <u>turn over and write it all down</u>.

1) Solve this inequality: $4X + 3 \leqslant 6X + 7$

2) Find all integer values p, such that a) $p^2 < 49$ b) $-20 < 4p \leqslant 17$

Graphical Inequalities

This is easy so long as you remember the easy method for drawing graphs — i.e. a table of 3 values (see P.41).

The questions always involve <u>SHADING A REGION ON A GRAPH</u>, which is actually easy but it's always presented as some really horrid-looking algebra that puts most people right off before they even start.

The thing is, once you realise that the horrid-looking algebra just means something really simple then the whole thing becomes quite mind-numbingly simple. . .

Method

1) <u>CONVERT each INEQUALITY to an EQUATION</u>

by simply putting an "=" in place of the "<", ">", "≤" or "≥".

2) <u>DO A TABLE OF 3 VALUES FOR EACH EQUATION</u> (See P.41)

and then <u>draw the lines</u> on the graph.

3) <u>SHADE THE DEFINED REGION</u>

The lines you've drawn enclose the defined region
— and they nearly always ask you to <u>shade it</u>.

Example

"Shade the region represented by : $\quad y \leq x + 2, \quad x + y \leq 5 \quad$ and $\quad y \geq 0$"

(See what I mean about the horrid-looking algebra?)

<u>*ANSWER:*</u>

1) <u>CONVERT EACH INEQUALITY TO AN *EQUATION*</u>:
$\quad y \leq x + 2 \quad$ becomes $\quad y = x + 2$,
$\quad x + y \leq 5 \quad$ becomes $\quad x + y = 5$,
$\quad\quad y \geq 0 \quad$ becomes $\quad y = 0$

2) <u>DO A TABLE OF 3 VALUES</u> for each equation, and draw the lines on a graph.
e.g. for $y = x + 2$:

X	0	2	4
Y	2	4	6

3) <u>SHADE THE DEFINED REGION</u>,
and Bob's your Uncle, it's done.

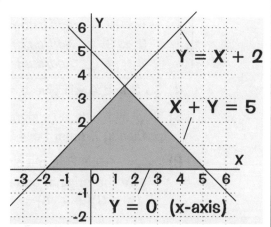

The Acid Test:

LEARN the <u>Three Steps</u> for doing <u>graphical inequalities</u>, then <u>turn over</u> and <u>write them down</u>.

1) Show on a graph the region enclosed by the following three conditions:
$$X + Y < 6, \quad Y > 0.5, \quad Y < 2X - 2$$

Factorising Quadratics

A quadratic equation has a variable raised to the power 2, but nothing higher than to the power 2, e.g. $2x^2 + x = 4$, $y^2 = 3y + 1$. There are several ways of solving a quadratic equation as detailed on the following pages. You need to know all the methods.

Factorising a Quadratic

"Factorising a quadratic" means "putting it into 2 brackets" — you'll need to remember that.

(There are several different methods for doing this, so stick with the one you're happiest with. If you have no preference then learn the one below.)

The standard format for quadratic equations is: $ax^2 + bx + c = 0$
Some Exam questions have $a = 1$, making them much easier.
       E.g. $x^2 + 3x + 2 = 0$ (See next page for when a is not 1.)

Factorising Method When a = 1

1) ALWAYS rearrange into the STANDARD FORMAT: $ax^2 + bx + c = 0$

2) Write down the TWO BRACKETS with the x's in: $(x \quad)(x \quad)=0$

3) Then find 2 numbers that MULTIPLY to give "c" (the end number) but also ADD/SUBTRACT to give "b" (the coefficient of x).

4) Put them in and check that the +/– signs work out properly.

An Example   *"Solve $x^2 - x = 12$ by factorising."*

ANSWER: 1) First rearrange it (into the standard format): $x^2 - x - 12 = 0$

2) a=1, so the initial brackets are: $(x \quad)(x \quad)=0$

3) We now want to look at all pairs of numbers that multiply to give "c" (=12), but which also add or subtract to give the value of b:

1×12	Add/subtract to give:	13 or 11
2×6	Add/subtract to give:	8 or 4
3×4	Add/subtract to give:	7 or ① ← *this is what we're after (=±b)*

4) So 3 and 4 will give b = ±1, so put them in: $(x \quad 3)(x \quad 4)=0$

5) Now fill in the +/– signs so that the 3 and 4 add/subtract to give –1 (=b), Clearly it must be +3 and –4 so we'll have: $(x + 3)(x - 4)=0$

6) As an ESSENTIAL check, EXPAND the brackets out again to make sure they give the original equation:
   $(x + 3)(x - 4) = x^2 + 3x - 4x - 12 = x^2 - x - 12$

We're not finished yet mind, because $(x + 3)(x - 4)=0$ is only the factorised form of the equation — we have yet to give the actual SOLUTIONS. This is very easy:

7) THE SOLUTIONS are simply the two numbers in the brackets, but with OPPOSITE +/– SIGNS: i.e. $x = -3$ or $+4$

Make sure you remember that last step. It's the difference between SOLVING THE EQUATION and merely factorising it.

Factorising Quadratics

When "a" is not 1

E.g. $3x^2 + 5x + 2 = 0$

The basic method is still the same but it's <u>a lot messier</u>. Chances are, the Exam question will be with a=1, so <u>make sure you can do that type easily</u>. Only then should you try to get to grips with these harder ones.

An Example

"Solve $3x^2 + 7x = 6$ by factorising."

1) <u>First rearrange it</u> (into the standard format): $\underline{3x^2 + 7x - 6 = 0}$

2) Now because a = 3, the two x-terms in the brackets will have to multiply to give $3x^2$, so the initial brackets will have to be: $\underline{(3x\quad)(x\quad)=0}$

   (i.e. <u>you put in the x-terms first</u>, with coefficients that will multiply to give "a").

3) We now want to look at <u>all pairs of numbers</u> that <u>multiply together to give "c"</u> (=6, ignoring the minus sign for now): i.e. 1×6 and 2×3

4) <u>*Now the difficult bit*</u>: to find the combination which does this:

   > <u>multiply with the 3x and x terms in the brackets and then</u>
   > <u>add or subtract to give the value of b (=7)</u>:

   The best way to do this is by trying out all the possibilities in the brackets until you find the combination that works. Don't forget that **EACH PAIR** of numbers can be tried in **TWO** different positions

(3x 1)(x 6)	<u>multiplies</u> to give <u>18x and 1x</u>	which <u>add/subtract</u> to give <u>19x or 17x</u>
(3x 6)(x 1)	<u>multiplies</u> to give <u>3x and 6x</u>	which <u>add/subtract</u> to give <u>9x or 3x</u>
(3x 3)(x 2)	<u>multiplies</u> to give <u>6x and 3x</u>	which <u>add/subtract</u> to give <u>9x or 3x</u>
(3x 2)(x 3)	<u>multiplies</u> to give <u>9x and 2x</u>	which <u>add/subtract</u> to give <u>11x or (7x)</u>

   So (3x 2)(x 3) is the combination that gives b = 7 (give or take a +/–).

5) <u>Now fill in the +/– signs</u> so that the combination will add/subtract to give +7 (=b). Clearly it must be +3 and –2 which gives rise to +9x and –2x.
   So the final brackets are: $\underline{(3x - 2)(x + 3)}$

6) <u>As an ESSENTIAL check, EXPAND the brackets</u> out again to make sure they give the original equation:

   $$(3x - 2)(x + 3) = 3x^2 + 9x - 2x - 6 = \underline{3x^2 + 7x - 6}$$

7) The last step is to get <u>THE SOLUTIONS TO THE EQUATION</u>: $(3x - 2)(x + 3)=0$

   which you do <u>by separately putting each bracket = 0</u> :

   i.e. $(3x - 2)=0 \Rightarrow \underline{x = 2/3}$ $\qquad\qquad (x + 3)=0 \Rightarrow \underline{x = -3}$

   Don't forget that last step. <u>Again, it's the difference</u> between <u>SOLVING THE EQUATION</u> and merely <u>factorising it</u>.

The Acid Test:

LEARN the <u>7 steps</u> for solving quadratics by <u>factorising</u>, both for "a = 1" and "a ≠ 1".

1) Solve these <u>by the factor method</u>: a) $x^2 + 5x - 24 = 0$ b) $x^2 - 6x + 9 = 16$
   c) $(x + 3)^2 - 3 = 13$ d) $5x^2 - 17x - 12 = 0$

The Quadratic Formula

The solutions to any quadratic equation $\underline{ax^2 + bx + c = 0}$ are given by this formula:

$$x = \frac{-b \pm \sqrt{b^2 - 4ac}}{2a}$$

<u>LEARN THIS FORMULA</u> — If you can't learn it, there's no way you'll be able to use it in the Exam, even if they give it to you.   Using it should, in principle, be quite straightforward. As it turns out though there are quite a few pitfalls, so <u>TAKE HEED of these crucial details</u>:

Using The Quadratic Formula

1) Always write it down in stages as you go. Take it nice and slowly — any fool can rush it and get it wrong, but there's no marks for being a clot.

2) <u>MINUS SIGNS</u>. Throughout the whole of algebra, minus signs cause untold misery <u>because people keep forgetting them</u>. In this formula, there are two minus signs that people keep forgetting: <u>the -b and the -4ac</u>.

   The -4ac causes particular problems <u>when either "a" or "c" is negative</u>, because it makes the -4ac effectively +4ac — <u>so learn to spot it as a HAZARD before it happens</u>.

   WHENEVER YOU GET A MINUS SIGN, <u>THE ALARM BELLS SHOULD ALWAYS RING!</u>

3) Remember you <u>divide ALL of the top line by 2a</u>, not just half of it.

4) Don't forget it's <u>2a</u> on the bottom line, not just a. This is another common mistake.

EXAMPLE:
"<u>Find the solutions of $3x^2 + 7x = 1$ to 2 decimal places.</u>"
(The mention of decimal places in exam questions is a VERY BIG CLUE to use the formula rather than trying to factorise it!)

Method
1) First get it into the form $\underline{ax^2 + bx + c = 0}$: $3x^2 + 7x - 1 = 0$
2) Then carefully identify a, b and c: $\underline{a = 3, \ b = 7, \ c = -1}$
3) Put these values into the quadratic formula and <u>write down each stage</u>:

$$x = \frac{-b \pm \sqrt{b^2 - 4ac}}{2a} = \frac{-7 \pm \sqrt{7^2 - 4 \times 3 \times -1}}{2 \times 3} = \frac{-7 \pm \sqrt{49 + 12}}{6}$$

add / subtract!

$$= \frac{-7 \pm \sqrt{61}}{6} = 0.1350 \text{ or } -2.468$$

So to 2 DP, the solutions are: <u>x = 0.14 or -2.47</u>

4) Finally <u>AS A CHECK</u> put these values back into the <u>original equation</u>:
E.g. for x = 0.1350: $3 \times 0.135^2 + 7 \times 0.135 = 0.999675$, which is 1, as near as ...

The Acid Test: LEARN the <u>4 CRUCIAL DETAILS</u> and the <u>4 STEPS OF THE METHOD</u> for using the Quadratic Formula, then <u>TURN OVER AND WRITE THEM ALL DOWN.</u>

1) Find the solutions of these equations (to 2 DP) using the quadratic formula:
   a) $x^2 + 10x - 4 = 0$ b) $3x^2 - 3x = 2$ c) $(2x + 3)^2 = 15$

Completing The Square

$$x^2 + 12x - 5 = (x + 6)^2 - 41$$

The SQUARE...   ...COMPLETED

Solving Quadratics by "Completing The Square"

This is quite a clever way of solving quadratics, but is perhaps a bit confusing at first. The name "Completing the Square" doesn't help — it's called that because of the method where you basically
1) _write down a SQUARED bracket, and then_
2) _stick a number on the end to "COMPLETE" it._
It's quite easy really, so long as you make an effort to learn all the steps — some of them aren't all that obvious.

Method

1) As always, <u>REARRANGE THE QUADRATIC INTO THE STANDARD FORMAT:</u>
$$ax^2 + bx + c = 0$$

2) <u>If "a" is not 1 then divide the whole equation by "a"</u> to make sure it is!

3) Now <u>WRITE OUT THE INITIAL BRACKET:</u> $(x + b/2)^2$

   <u>NB: THE NUMBER IN THE BRACKET</u> is always <u>HALF THE (NEW) VALUE OF "b"</u>

4) <u>MULTIPLY OUT THE BRACKETS</u> and <u>COMPARE TO THE ORIGINAL</u>
   to find what extra is needed, and add or subtract the adjusting amount.

Example: _"Express $x^2 - 6x - 7 = 0$ as a completed square, and hence solve it."_

The equation is already in the standard form and "a" = 1, so:

1) The coefficient of x is -6, so the squared brackets must be: $(x - 3)^2$

2) <u>Multiply out the brackets:</u> $x^2 - 6x + 9$, <u>and compare</u> with the original: $x^2 - 6x - 7$.
   To make it like the original equation it needs -16 on the end, hence we get:

$(x - 3)^2 - 16 = 0$	as the alternative version of $x^2 - 6x - 7 = 0$

We want to <u>SOLVE</u> this equation, so we need these 3 special steps:

1) <u>Take the 16 over</u> to get: $(x - 3)^2 = 16$

2) Then <u>SQUARE ROOT BOTH SIDES:</u> $(x - 3) = \pm 4$ <u>AND DON'T FORGET THE $\pm$</u>

3) <u>Take the 3 over</u> to get: $x = \pm 4 + 3$ <u>so x = 7 or -1</u> _(again don't forget the $\pm$)_

The Acid Test: LEARN the <u>4 STEPS OF THE METHOD</u> for completing the square and the <u>3 SPECIAL STEPS</u> for <u>SOLVING THE EQUATION</u> you get from it.

1) <u>Now turn over and write it all down</u> to see what you've <u>learned</u>.   (Frightening, isn't it?)

2) Find the solutions of these equations (to 2 DP) by completing the square:
   a) $x^2 + 10x - 4 = 0$ b) $3x^2 - 3x = 2$

Simultaneous Equations

Simultaneous equations tend to follow a pretty standard format and the rules are really quite simple, but <u>you must follow ALL the steps, in the right order, and treat them as a strict method</u>.

Every step is vital. Miss one out and it's like forgetting to put the water in with the sand and cement — no matter how well you pummel the mixture, it won't stick your bricks together.

There are two types of simultaneous equations you could get
— EASY ONES (where both equations are linear) and TRICKY ONES (where one's quadratic).

(1) $2x = 6 - 4y$ and $-3 - 3y = 4x$ (2) $7x + y = 1$ and $2x^2 - y = 3$

(1) Six Steps For EASY Simultaneous Equations

We'll use these two equations for our example: $2x = 6 - 4y$ and $-3 - 3y = 4x$

1) <u>Rearrange both equations into the form</u>   <u>$ax + by = c$</u>   where a,b,c are numbers (which can be negative). Also label the two equations —(1) and —(2)

$$2x + 4y = 6 \qquad —(1)$$
$$-4x - 3y = 3 \qquad —(2)$$

2) You need to <u>match up the numbers in front</u> (the "coefficients") of either the x's or y's in both equations. To do this you may need to multiply one or both equations by a suitable number. You should then relabel them: —(3) and —(4)

(1)×2 : $4x + 8y = 12 \qquad — (3)$
$$-4x - 3y = 3 \qquad — (4)$$

3) <u>Add or subtract the two equations</u> to eliminate the terms with the same coefficient.
If the <u>coefficients are the same</u> (both +ve or both –ve) then <u>SUBTRACT</u>.
If the <u>coefficients are opposite</u> (one +ve and one –ve) then <u>ADD</u>.

(3) + (4) $0x + 5y = 15$

4) Solve the resulting equation to find whichever letter is left in it.

$$5y = 15 \implies \underline{y = 3}$$

5) Substitute this value back into equation (1) and solve it to find the other quantity.

Sub in (1): $2x + 4 \times 3 = 6 \implies 2x + 12 = 6 \implies 2x = -6 \implies \underline{x = -3}$

6) Then substitute both these values into equation (2) to make sure it works out properly. If it doesn't then you've done something wrong and you'll have to do it all again.

Sub x and y in (2) : $-4 \times -3 - 3 \times 3 = 12 - 9 = \underline{3}$, which is right, so it's worked.
So the solutions are: $\underline{x = -3}$, $\underline{y = 3}$

The Acid Test:
LEARN the 6 Steps for solving EASY Simultaneous Equations.

1)   Remember, you only know them when you can write them all out from memory, so turn over the page and see if you can write down all six steps. Then try again.

2) Then apply the 6 steps to find F and G given that
$$2F - 10 = 4G \qquad \text{and} \qquad 3G = 4F - 15.$$

Simultaneous Equations

② Seven Steps For TRICKY Simultaneous Equations

Example: Solve these two equations simultaneously: $7x + y = 1$ and $2x^2 - y = 3$

1) Rearrange the quadratic equation so that you have one term on its own. And label the equations ① and ② .

$$7x + y = 1 \qquad — ①$$
$$y = 2x^2 - 3 \qquad — ②$$

2) Substitute the quadratic expression into the other equation. You'll get another equation — label it ③ .

$$7x + y = 1 \qquad — ①$$
$$y = (2x^2 - 3) \qquad — ②$$
$$7x + (2x^2 - 3) = 1 \qquad — ③$$

In this example you just shove the expression for y into equation ①, in place of y.

3) Rearrange to get a quadratic equation. And guess what... You've got to solve it.

Remember — if it won't factorise, you can either use the formula or complete the square. Have a look at P.56-57 for more details.

$$2x^2 + 7x - 4 = 0$$

That factorises into:
$$(2x - 1)(x + 4) = 0$$

Check this step by multiplying out again:
$(2x - 1)(x + 4) = 2x^2 - x + 8x - 4 = 2x^2 + 7x - 4$ ☺

So, $2x - 1 = 0$ OR $x + 4 = 0$
In other words, $\underline{x = 0.5}$ OR $\underline{x = -4}$

4) Stick the first value back in one of the original equations (pick the easy one).

① $7x + y = 1$ Substitute in x = 0.5: $3.5 + y = 1$, so $\underline{y = 1 - 3.5 = -2.5}$

5) Stick the second value back in the same original equation (the easy one again).

① $7x + y = 1$ Substitute in x = -4: $-28 + y = 1$, so $\underline{y = 1 + 28 = 29}$

6) Substitute both pairs of answers back into the other original equation to check they work.

② $y = 2x^2 - 3$

Substitute in x = 0.5 and y = -2.5: $-2.5 = (2 \times 0.25) - 3 = -2.5$ — jolly good.
Substitute in x = -4 and y = 29: $29 = (2 \times 16) - 3 = 29$ — *smashing.*

7) Write the pairs of answers out again, *CLEARLY*, at the bottom of your working.

The two pairs of answers are: $\underline{x = 0.5 \text{ and } y = -2.5}$ OR $\underline{x = -4 \text{ and } y = 29}$

(Do this even if you think it's pointless and stupid. If there's even the remotest chance of the examiner getting the pairs mixed up, it's worth a tiny bit of extra effort, don't you think?)

The Acid Test:

LEARN the 7 Steps for solving TRICKY Simultaneous Equations.

Apply the 7 steps to find f and g, given that:

a) $f = g^2 + 4$ and $f - 6g - 4 = 0$ b) $13g - f = -7$ and $3g^2 - f = 3$
c) $4g + f = 3$ and $f = 4g^2$ d) $g = 4f^2 - 3$ and $g + 11f = 0$

Trial and Improvement

Basically, this is an easy way to find approximate answers to quite complicated equations. BUT......you have to make an effort to <u>LEARN THE FINER DETAILS</u> of this method, otherwise you'll never get the hang of it.

Method

1) <u>SUBSTITUTE TWO INITIAL VALUES</u> into the equation that give <u>OPPOSITE CASES</u>. *These are usually suggested in the question. If not, you'll have to think of your own. "Opposite cases" means <u>one answer too big, one too small</u>, or <u>one +ve, one −ve</u>, for example. If your values don't give opposite cases, <u>try again</u>.*

2) Now CHOOSE YOUR NEXT VALUE <u>IN BETWEEN</u> THE PREVIOUS TWO, and <u>SUBSTITUTE it into the equation</u>.
<u>Continue this process</u>, always choosing a new value <u>between the two closest opposite cases</u>, (and preferably nearer to the one which is closest to the answer you want).

3) <u>AFTER ONLY 3 OR 4 STEPS</u> you should have <u>2 numbers</u> which are to the <u>right degree of accuracy but DIFFER BY 1 IN THE LAST DIGIT</u>.
For example if you had to get your answer to 2 DP then you'd eventually end up with say 5.43 and 5.44, with these giving OPPOSITE results of course.

4) <u>At this point</u> you ALWAYS take the <u>Exact Middle Value</u> to decide which is the answer you want. *E.g. for 5.43 and 5.44, you'd try 5.435 to see if the real answer was <u>between 5.43 and 5.435</u> or between <u>5.435 and 5.44</u> (See below).*

Example:

The equation $X^2 + X = 14$ has a solution between 3 and 3.5. Find this solution to 1 DP.

Try X = 3	$3^2 + 3 = 12$	(Too small)
Try X = 3.5	$3.5^2 + 3.5 = 15.75$	(Too big)

← (2 opposite cases)

14 is what we want and it's slightly closer to 15.75 than it is to 12 so we'll choose our next value for X a bit closer to 3.5 than 3

Try X = 3.3	$3.3^2 + 3.3 = 14.19$	(Too big)

Good, this is very close, but we need to see if 3.2 is still too big or too small:

Try X = 3.2	$3.2^2 + 3.2 = 13.44$	(Too small)

Good, now we know that <u>the answer must be between 3.2 and 3.3</u>. To Find out which one it's nearest to, we have to try the <u>EXACT MIDDLE VALUE</u>:   3.25

Try X = 3.25	$3.25^2 + 3.25 = 13.81$	(Too small)

This tells us that the solution must be between 3.25 (too small) and 3.3 (too big), and so to 1 DP <u>it must round up to 3.3</u>.   <u>ANSWER = 3.3</u>

The Acid Test:
"LEARN and TURN" — If you don't actually <u>commit it to memory</u>, then you've wasted your time even reading it.

To succeed with this method you must <u>LEARN the 4 steps above</u>. Do it now, and practise until you can <u>write them down without having to look back at them</u>. It's not as difficult as you think.

1) The equation $X^2 - 2X = 1$ has a solution between 2 and 3. Find it to 1 DP.

Five Graphs You Should Recognise

There are five graphs that you should know the basic shape of just from looking at their equations — it really isn't as difficult as it sounds.

1) STRAIGHT LINE GRAPHS: "y = mx + c" (Note, no x² or x³ or ¹⁄ₓ in the equation)

You should know plenty about these — all of P.62-P.63 in fact — so make sure you do.

EXAMPLES: $y = 3x+2$, $3y - 3 = x$, $4x - 5 +2y = 0$, $x - y = 12$

2) X² BUCKET SHAPES: $Y = ax^2 + bx + c$ (where b and/or c can be zero)

Notice that all these graphs have the <u>same SYMMETRICAL bucket shape</u> and that if the x² bit has a "–" in front of it then the bucket is *upside down*.

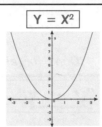

$Y = X^2$

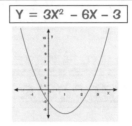

$Y = 3X^2 - 6X - 3$

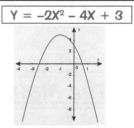

$Y = -2X^2 - 4X + 3$

3) X³ GRAPHS: $Y = ax^3 + bx^2 + cx + d$ (Note that b, c and/or d can be zero)

(Note that x³ must be the highest power and there must be no other bits like ¹⁄ₓ etc.)

All X³ graphs have the *same basic wiggle* in the middle, but it can be a flat wiggle or a more pronounced wiggle. Notice that "<u>–X³ graphs</u>" always come <u>down from top left</u> whereas the <u>+X³</u> ones go <u>up from bottom left</u>.

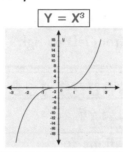

$Y = X^3$

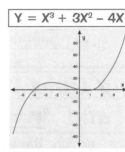

$Y = X^3 + 3X^2 - 4X$

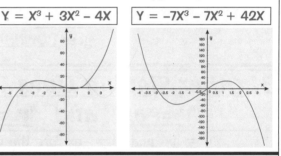

$Y = -7X^3 - 7X^2 + 42X$

4) 1/X GRAPHS: $Y = \frac{A}{X}$, or $XY = A$, where A is some number (+ or –)

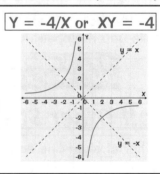

$Y = 4/X$ or $XY = 4$

These graphs are <u>all the same basic shape</u>, except that the negative ones are in the opposite quadrants to the positive ones (as shown). The two halves of the graph don't touch. They're all <u>symmetrical about the lines y=x and y=-x</u>.

This is also the type of graph you get with <u>inverse proportion</u>. (See P.38)

$Y = -4/X$ or $XY = -4$

5) Kˣ GRAPHS: $Y = K^X$, where K is some positive number

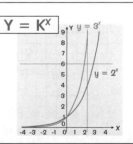

$Y = K^X$

1) These graphs *curve upwards* when K > 1.

2) They're always *above the x-axis*.

3) They all *go through the point (0, 1)*.

4) For *bigger values of K*, the graph *tails off towards zero more quickly* on the left and *climbs more steeply* on the right.

The Acid Test:

LEARN the <u>5 Types of Graph</u>, both their equations and their shapes, then turn over and <u>sketch three examples of each</u>.

1) Describe the following graphs *in words*: a) $y = 3x^2 + 2$ b) $y = 4 - x^3$ c) $yx = 2$
d) $x + 2y = 6$ e) $x = -7/y$ f) $3x^2 = y - 4x^3 + 2$ g) $y = x - x^2$ h) $y = 5^x$

Straight Lines You Should Just Know

You ought to know these simple graphs straight off with no hesitation:

1) Horizontal and Vertical lines: "x = a" and "y = b"

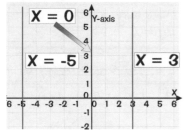

☞ x = a is a <u>vertical line</u> <u>through "a"</u> on the x-axis

y = a is a <u>horizontal line</u> <u>through "a"</u> on the y-axis ☜

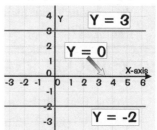

Don't forget: <u>the y-axis is also the line x=0</u>

Don't forget: <u>the x-axis is also the line y=0</u>

2) The Main Diagonals: "y = x" and "y = –x"

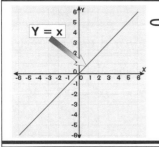

☞ "Y = X" is the <u>main diagonal</u> that goes <u>UPHILL</u> from left to right.

"Y = –X" is the <u>main diagonal</u> that goes <u>DOWNHILL</u> from left to right. ☜

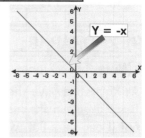

3) Other Sloping Lines Through the origin: "y = ax" and "y = –ax"

y = ax and y = -ax are the equations for **A SLOPING LINE THROUGH THE ORIGIN.**

The value of "*a*" is <u>the *GRADIENT* of the line</u>, so <u>the BIGGER the number, the STEEPER the slope</u> — and a MINUS SIGN tells you it slopes DOWNHILL, as shown by the ones here:

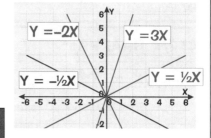

The gradient of a horizontal line (eg y = 3) is 0.
The gradient of a vertical line (eg x = 2) is ∞ (infinity — ooh).

All Other Straight Lines

Other straight-line equations are a little more complicated and the next two pages show three methods for drawing them. Mind you, the first step is identifying them in the first place. Remember:

All straight line equations just contain "*something x, something y, and a number*".

<u>Straight lines:</u>		<u>NOT straight lines:</u>	
x – y = 0	y = 2 + 3x	y = x³ + 3	2y – 1/x = 7
2y – 4x = 7	4x – 3 = 5y	1/y + 1/x = 2	x(3 – 2y) = 3
3y + 3x = 12	6y – x – 7 = 0	x² = 4 – y	xy + 3 =0
5(x + 3y) = 5	12x – 7 = 3(x + 4y)	2x + 3y = xy	Y = ½SIN X

The Acid Test:

<u>LEARN</u> all the specific graphs on this page and also how to <u>identify straight-line equations.</u>

Now turn over the page and write down everything you've learned.

Straight-Line Graphs: "y = mx + c"

Using "$y = mx + c$" is perhaps the "proper" way of dealing with straight-line equations, and it's a nice trick if you can do it. The first thing you have to do though is <u>rearrange the equation</u> into the standard format "$y = mx + c$" like this:

Straight line:		Rearranged into "$y = mx + c$"	
$y = 2 + 3x$	$\rightarrow$	$y = 3x + 2$	(m=3, c=2)
$2y - 4x = 7$	$\rightarrow$	$y = 2x + 3\frac{1}{2}$	(m=2, c=3½)
$x - y = 0$	$\rightarrow$	$y = x + 0$	(m=1, c=0)
$4x - 3 = 5y$	$\rightarrow$	$y = 0.8x - 0.6$	(m=0.8, c=-0.6)
$3y + 3x = 12$	$\rightarrow$	$y = -x + 4$	(m=-1, c=4)

REMEMBER: "<u>m</u>" equals the <u>GRADIENT</u> of the line.
                      "<u>c</u>" is the "<u>y-intercept</u>" (where the graph hits the y-axis).

<u>BUT WATCH OUT</u>: people mix up "m" and "c" when they get something like $y = 5 + 2x$.
<u>REMEMBER</u>, "m" is the number <u>IN FRONT OF THE "X"</u> and "c" is the number <u>ON ITS OWN</u>.

1) Sketching a Straight Line using y = mx + c

1) Get the equation into the form "<u>$y = mx + c$</u>".

2) <u>*Put a dot on the y-axis*</u> at the value of c.

3) Then go <u>ALONG ONE UNIT</u> and <u>*up or down by the value of m*</u> and make another dot.

4) <u>*Repeat*</u> the same "step" in <u>*both directions*</u>.

5) Finally check that the gradient LOOKS RIGHT.

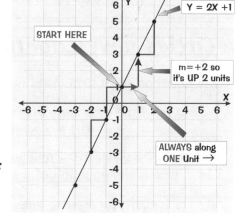

The graph shows the process for the equation "$y = 2x + 1$":
1) "c" = 1, so put a first dot at y = 1 on the y-axis.
2) Go along 1 unit → and then up by 2 because "m" = +2.
3) Repeat the same step, 1→ 2↑ in both directions.
4) CHECK: <u>*a gradient of +2*</u> *should be* <u>*quite steep and uphill left to right*</u> *which it is, so it looks OK.*

2) Finding the Equation of a Straight-Line Graph

This is the reverse process and it's <u>EASIER</u>.

1) From the axes, <u>*identify the two variables*</u> (e.g. "x and y" or "h and t").
2) <u>*Find the values*</u> of "<u>m</u>" (gradient) and "<u>c</u>" (y-intercept) from the graph.
3) Using these values from the graph, <u>*write down the equation*</u> with the standard format "$y = mx + c$".

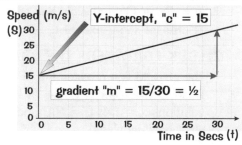

For the example above: "<u>$S = \frac{1}{2}t + 15$</u>"

The Acid Test:

<u>LEARN</u> what straight-line equations look like and the <u>8</u> <u>RULES</u> for drawing the lines and <u>finding the equations</u>.

1) Sketch these graphs: a) $y = 2 + x$ b) $y = x + 6$ c) $4x - 2y = 0$ d) $y = 1 - \frac{1}{2}x$
      e) $x = 2y + 4$ f) $2x - 6y - 8 = 0$ g) $0.4x - 0.2y = 0.5$ h) $y = 3 - x + 2$

Gradients and Graphs of Circles

Parallel Lines have the Same Gradients

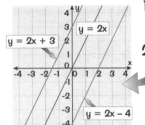

1) The equation of a straight line is $\underline{y = mx + c}$, where $\underline{m}$ is the gradient and c is the y-intercept.

2) Parallel lines have the same value of m — i.e. the same gradient.

EXAMPLE: The lines $y = 2x + 3$,
$\qquad\qquad\qquad y = 2x$
and $y = 2x - 4$ are all parallel.

Perpendicular Gradients are Linked

The gradients of two perpendicular lines multiply to give –1.

> If the gradient of the first line is m, the gradient of the other line will be $\dfrac{-1}{m}$, because $m \times \dfrac{-1}{m} = -1$.

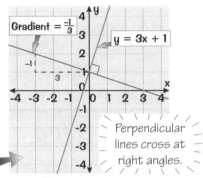

Perpendicular lines cross at right angles.

EXAMPLE: The line $y = 3x + 1$ has the gradient 3. A line which is perpendicular to this line will have the gradient $\dfrac{-1}{3}$.

Circles have Equations

The equation for a circle with centre (0, 0) and radius r is: $\boxed{x^2 + y^2 = r^2}$

E.g. $x^2 + y^2 = 4$ is a circle with centre (0, 0). $r^2 = 4$, so the radius, r, is 2.
$x^2 + y^2 = 100$ is a circle with centre (0, 0) too. $r^2 = 100$, so the radius, r, is 10.

You might be given two simultaneous equations to solve, where one is the equation of a circle. Eeek.

Example: "By drawing graphs, solve the simultaneous equations $x^2 + y^2 = 16$ and $y = 2x + 1$."

1) DRAW BOTH GRAPHS.
$x^2 + y^2 = 16$ is the equation of a circle, centre (0, 0) and radius $\sqrt{16} = 4$.
$y = 2x + 1$ is a straight line with gradient 2. It crosses the y-axis at 1.

2) LOOK FOR WHERE THE GRAPHS CROSS.
The straight line crosses the circle at two points. Reading the x and y values of these points gives the solutions x = 1.4, y = 3.8 and x = -2.2, y = –3.4 (to 1 decimal place).

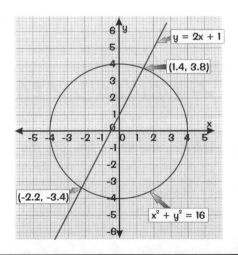

The Acid Test:

1) What are the gradients of lines perpendicular to these lines?
   a) $y = 4x + 3$ b) $y = \frac{1}{2}x - 5$ c) $y = 5 - 2x$

2) What are the radii of the following circles?
   a) $x^2 + y^2 = 1$ b) $x^2 + y^2 = 49$ c) $x^2 + y^2 = 20$

Finding Equations From Graphs

The basic idea here is to _get the equation for a given curve_ and there are _four main types_ of equation/curve which you're likely to get in the Exam:

SQUARED FUNCTION: "y = ax² + b"	**CUBIC FUNCTION:** "y = ax³ + b"
EXPONENTIAL FUNCTION: "y = pqˣ "	**TRIG FUNCTION:** "y = D(SIN X)+ E"

It can all seem quite tricky to the uninitiated but once you've cottoned on to the method it's really pretty simple. It's the same easy method for all of them and this is it:

Method

1) You have to find <u>TWO</u> unknowns in the equation (e.g. a and b, or p and q, etc.), which means you'll need <u>TWO</u> pairs of **X** and **Y** values to stick in the equation.

2) You find these simply by taking the _coordinates_ of _two points on the graph_.

3) You should always try to _take points that lie on either the X-axis or Y-axis_. (This makes one of the coordinates <u>ZERO</u> which makes the equations much easier to solve.)

Example

The graph below has been obtained from experimental data and the curve appears to be of the form "H = at² + b". Use the graph to find values for the constants "a" and "b".

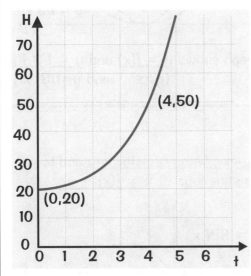

<u>ANSWER</u>:
We can choose any two points on the graph but the most obvious and sensible choices are the two indicated: (0,20) and (4,50).
The best of these of course is (0,20), and sticking these values for H and t in the equation gives:
$20 = 0 + b$, so straight away we know <u>b = 20</u>

Now using (4,50), together with b=20 gives:
$$50 = a \times 16 + 20$$
which gives: $a = (50 - 20)/16 = 1.875$ so <u>a = 1.9</u>
(to 2sf)

Hence the equation is $\boxed{H = 1.9t^2 + 20}$

If they give you one of the other equations, then the algebra will be a bit different. However, the basic method is always exactly the same so make sure you know it!

The Acid Test:

LEARN the <u>three points</u> of the method above.
Then <u>turn the page</u> and <u>write them down</u>.

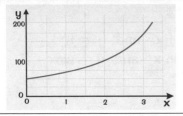

1) The graph shown here is thought to be represented by the equation $Y = PQ^x$ where P and Q are unknown constants. Use the graph to find the values of P and Q.

Graphs: Shifts and Stretches

Don't be put off by <u>function notation</u> involving f(x). It doesn't mean anything complicated, it's just a fancy way of saying "An expression in x".

In other words "y = f(x)" just means "y = some totally mundane expression in x, which we won't tell you, we'll just call it f(x) instead to see how many of you get in a flap about it".

In a question on transforming graphs they will either use <u>function notation</u> or they'll use a <u>known function</u> instead. <u>There are only four different types of graph transformations</u> so just <u>LEARN them and be done with it</u>. Here they are in order of difficulty:

1) *Y-Stretch*: $y = k \times f(x)$

This is where the original graph is <u>stretched along the y-axis</u> by multiplying the whole function by a number, <u>i.e. y = f(x) becomes y = kf(x)</u> (where k = 2 or 5 etc.). If k is less than 1, then the graph is <u>squashed down</u> in the y-direction instead:

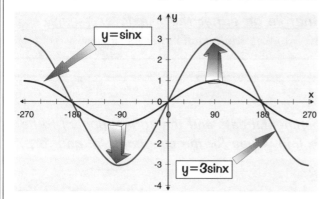

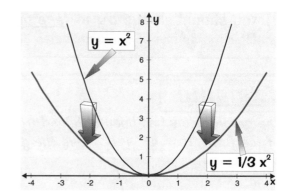

This graph shows <u>y = f(x) and y = 3f(x)</u>
(y = SIN X and Y = 3 SIN X)

This graph shows <u>y = f(x) and y = 1/3 f(x)</u>
(y=x² and y=1/3 x²)

2) *Y-Shift*: $y = f(x) + a$

This is where the whole graph is <u>slid UP OR DOWN the y-axis with no distortion</u>, and is achieved by simply <u>adding a number onto the end of the equation</u>:   y = f(x) + a.

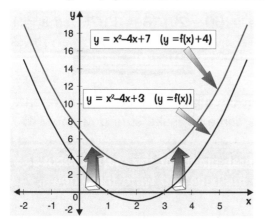

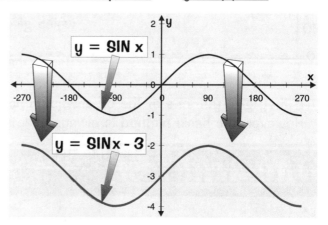

This shows <u>y = f(x) and y = f(x) + 4</u>
i.e. y = x² – 4x + 3, and
$$y = (x^2 - 4x + 3) + 4$$
or y = x² – 4x + 7

This shows <u>y = f(x)</u> and <u>y = f(x) – 3</u>
i.e   y = sin x   and   y = sinx – 3

Graphs: Shifts and Stretches

3) X-Shift: Y = f(x − a)

This is where <u>the whole graph slides to the left or right</u> and it only happens when you <u>replace "x"</u> everywhere in the equation <u>with "x − a"</u>. These are a bit tricky because they go "<u>the wrong way</u>". In other words if you want to go from <u>y = f(x) to y = f(x − a)</u> you must move the whole graph a distance "a" in the <u>POSITIVE</u> X-direction → (and vice versa).

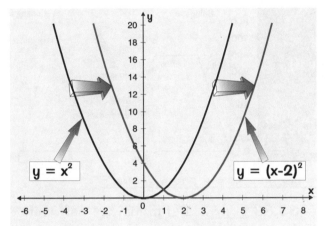

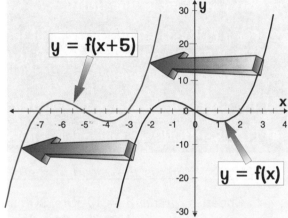

This graph shows <u>y=f(x)</u> and <u>y=f(x−2)</u>
(i.e. y =x² and y =(x−2)²)

This graph shows <u>y=f(x)</u> and <u>y=f(x+5)</u>
i.e. y=x³ − 4x, and y=(x+5)³ − 4(x+5)

4) X-Stretch: Y = f(kX)

These go "<u>the wrong way</u>" too — when k is a "<u>multiplier</u>" it <u>*scrunches the graph up*</u>, whereas when it's a "<u>divider</u>", it <u>*stretches*</u> the graph out. (The opposite of the y-stretch)

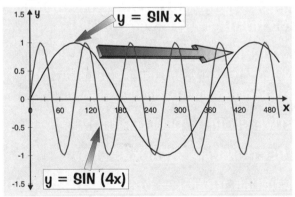

This graph shows <u>y = SIN X</u> and <u>y = SIN(4X)</u>. The one that is all squashed up is y = SIN(4X). With a multiplier of 4 it will be 4 times as squashed up. This helps you sketch the graph. *(Each full cycle of up-and-down takes ¼ the amount of x-axis as the original graph, so you fit 4 of them into 1 of the other graph.)*

Remember, if k is a <u>divider</u>, then the graph <u>spreads out</u>. So if the squashed up graph above was the original, <u>y = f(x)</u>, then the more spread out one would be <u>y = f(x/4)</u>.

The Acid Test:

LEARN the <u>Four types of Graph Transformations</u>, both the effect on the formula and the effect on the graph. <u>Then turn over</u> and <u>draw two examples of each type</u>.

1) Sketch these graphs: a) y = x²   b) y = x² − 4   c) y = 3x²   d) y = (x − 3)²
   e) y = cos x   f) y = cos (x + 30⁰)   g) y = cosx + 3   h) y = 2cosx − 4

D/T Graphs and V/T Graphs

Distance-time graphs and *Velocity-time graphs* are so common in Exams that they deserve a page all to themselves *just to make sure you know all the vital details* about them. The best thing about them is that they don't vary much and they're always easy.

1) Distance-Time Graphs

Just remember these 4 important points:

1) At any point, <u>GRADIENT</u> = <u>SPEED</u>, but watch out for the <u>UNITS</u>.

2) For a <u>CURVED GRAPH</u> you'll need to draw a <u>TANGENT</u> to work out the <u>SPEED</u> (gradient) at any particular point.

3) The <u>STEEPER</u> the graph, the <u>FASTER</u> it's going.

4) <u>FLAT SECTIONS</u> are where it is <u>STOPPED</u>.

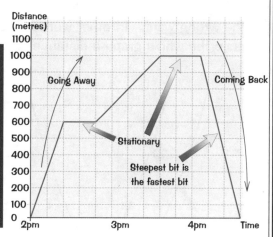

<u>EXAMPLE:</u> *"What is the speed of the return section on the graph shown?"*

Speed = gradient = 1000m/30mins = **33.33** <u>m/min</u>. But m/min are naff units so it's better to do it like this: 1km ÷ 0.5 hrs = <u>2 km/h</u>

2) Velocity-Time Graphs

A *Velocity-Time graph* can <u>LOOK</u> just the same as a *Distance-Time graph* but means something *completely different*. The graph shown here is exactly the same SHAPE as the one above, *but the actual motions are completely different*.

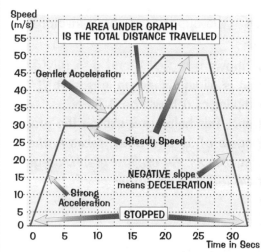

Remember these 5 important points:

1) At any point, <u>GRADIENT = ACCELERATION</u> (The UNITS are m/s² don't forget).

2) For a <u>CURVED GRAPH</u> you'll need to draw a <u>TANGENT</u> to work out the <u>ACCELERATION</u> (gradient) at any particular point.

3) <u>NEGATIVE SLOPE</u> is <u>DECELERATION</u>.

4) <u>FLAT SECTIONS</u> are <u>STEADY SPEED</u>.

5) <u>AREA UNDER GRAPH = DISTANCE TRAVELLED</u>

The *D/T graph* shows something *moving away and then back again* with *steady speeds* and *long stops*, rather like a *DONKEY ON BLACKPOOL BEACH*. The *V/T graph* on the other hand shows something that *sets off from rest*, *accelerates strongly*, *holds its speed*, then *accelerates again up to a maximum speed* which it holds for a while and then *comes to a dramatic halt at the end*. *MORE LIKE A <u>FERRARI</u> THAN A DONKEY!*

The Acid Test:

LEARN the <u>9 IMPORTANT POINTS</u> and the <u>TWO DIAGRAMS</u> then <u>turn over</u> and <u>write them all down</u>.

1) For the D/T graph shown above, work out the speed of the middle section in km/h.
2) For the V/T graph, work out the three different accelerations and the two steady speeds.

Areas

It's true that you might get given some of these formulas in the exam, but I GUARANTEE that if you don't learn them beforehand, you'll be <u>totally incapable</u> of using them in the exam — <u>REMEMBER, I ABSOLUTELY GUARANTEE IT</u> !

You must LEARN these Formulas:

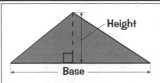

<u>Area of triangle</u> = ½ × base × vertical height

Note that the <u>height</u> must always be the <u>vertical height</u>, not the sloping height.

$$A = ½ × b × h_v$$

The alternative formula is this:
<u>Area of triangle</u> = ½ abSINC

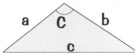

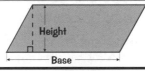

<u>Area of parallelogram</u> = base × vertical height

$$A = b × h_v$$

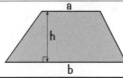

<u>Area of trapezium</u> = average of parallel sides × distance between them

$$A = ½ × (a + b) × h$$

<u>Area of circle</u> = π × (radius)² $\quad A = π × r^2$

<u>Circumference</u> = π × Diameter $\quad C = π × D$

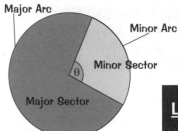

<u>Area of Sector</u> = $\dfrac{θ}{360}$ × Area of full Circle

(Pretty obvious really isn't it?)

<u>Length of Arc</u> = $\dfrac{θ}{360}$ × Circumference of full Circle

(Obvious again, no?)

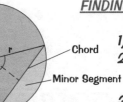

<u>FINDING THE AREA OF A SEGMENT</u> is a slightly involved business but worth learning:

1) Find the <u>area of the sector</u> using the above formula.
2) Find the area of the triangle using the formula ½absinC.
*   In this case it's ½r²sinθ.*

3) Then just <u>subtract</u> the area of the triangle from the area of the sector.

The Acid Test:

LEARN THIS PAGE – Then <u>turn over and write</u> down all the important details. Check your effort and <u>try again</u>.

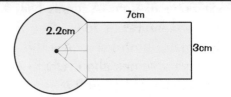

1) <u>Find the perimeter and area of this shape</u>. As for any exam question on area, you will need to make use of <u>Pythagoras and/or trigonometry</u> to solve this one. (See P.81 & 83-84.)

Volumes

VOLUME FORMULAS — YOU MUST LEARN THESE TOO!

1) _Sphere_

Volume of sphere $= \frac{4}{3}\pi r^3$

EXAMPLE: The moon has a radius of 1700km. Find its volume.

Ans: $V = \frac{4}{3}\pi r^3 = (4/3) \times \pi \times 1700^3 = \underline{2.1 \times 10^{10}} \text{ km}^3$ (A lot of cheese)

2) _Prisms_

A PRISM is a solid (3-D) object which has a <u>constant area of cross-section</u> — i.e. it's the same shape all the way through.

Now strangely, a lot of people aren't really sure what prisms are, but they come up a lot in Exams, <u>so make sure YOU know</u>.

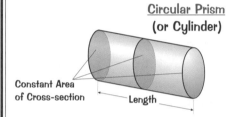

Circular Prism
(or Cylinder)

Constant Area
of Cross-section — Length

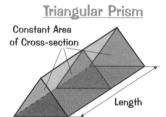

Triangular Prism

Constant Area
of Cross-section

Length

Hexagonal Prism
(a flat one, certainly, but still a prism)

Length

Constant Area
of Cross-section

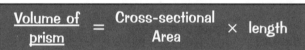

$$\frac{\text{Volume of}}{\text{prism}} = \frac{\text{Cross-sectional}}{\text{Area}} \times \text{length}$$

$$V = A \times l$$

3) _Pyramids and Cones_

Cone

Square-based
Pyramid

Tetrahedron

A pyramid is any shape that goes up to a point at the top. Its base can be any shape at all. If the base is a circle then it's called a cone (rather than a circular pyramid).

Volume of Pyramid $= \frac{1}{3} \times$ Base Area $\times$ Height

Volume of Cone $= \frac{1}{3} \times \pi r^2 \times$ Height

This surprisingly simple formula is true for any pyramid or cone, whether it goes up "vertically" (like the three shown here) or off to one side (like the one in the Acid Test below).

A Frustum _is_ Part of a Cone

A <u>frustum of a cone</u> is what's left when the top part of a cone is cut off parallel to its base.

$$\frac{\text{Volume of}}{\text{frustum}} = \frac{\text{Volume of the}}{\text{original cone}} - \frac{\text{Volume of the}}{\text{removed cone}}$$

$$= \frac{1}{3}\pi R^2 H - \frac{1}{3}\pi r^2 h$$

The Acid Test:

LEARN this page. Then turn over and try to write it all down. <u>Keep trying until you can do it.</u>

1) Name these three shapes and find their volumes:

a)

4cm
3cm
7cm
9cm

b)

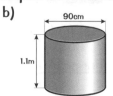
90cm
1.1m

c)

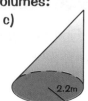
4m
2.2m

2) A ping pong ball has a diameter of 4cm. A tennis ball has a diameter of 7cm. Find the volume of both balls. Are the relative volumes about what you would expect? (See P.78)

Length, Area and Volume

Identifying Formulas Just by Looking at Them

This is pretty easy since we're only talking about the formulas for 3 things:
LENGTH, AREA and VOLUME, and the rules are as simple as this:

> AREA FORMULAS always have lengths MULTIPLIED IN PAIRS.
>
> VOLUME FORMULAS always have lengths MULTIPLIED IN GROUPS OF THREE.
>
> LENGTH FORMULAS (such as perimeter) always have LENGTHS OCCURRING SINGLY.

In formulas of course, *lengths are represented by letters*, so when you look at a formula you're *looking for groups of letters MULTIPLIED together* in ones, twos or threes.
BUT REMEMBER, π is *NOT a length* so don't count it as one of your letters.

EXAMPLES:

	πd (length)	2l + 2w (length)	4π(a + b)² (area)
πr² (area)	(4/3)πr³ (volume)	3b(d + l)² (volume)	4πr² + 6d² (area)
4πr + 15L (length)	Lwh + 6r²L (volume)	$\frac{5ph^2 + d^3}{4\pi r}$ (area)	5p²L − 4k³/7 (volume)
2πd − 14r/3 (length)	6hp + πr² + 7h² (area)		

Surface Area And Nets

1) <u>SURFACE AREA</u> only applies to solid 3D objects, and it is simply <u>the total area of all the outer surfaces added together</u>. If you were painting it, it's all the bits you'd paint.

2) There is <u>NEVER A SIMPLE FORMULA</u> for surface area — <u>you have to work out each side in turn and then ADD THEM ALL TOGETHER.</u>

3) <u>A NET</u> is just <u>A SOLID SHAPE FOLDED OUT FLAT.</u>

4) So obviously :   <u>SURFACE AREA OF SOLID = AREA OF NET.</u>

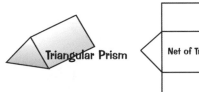
Triangular Prism

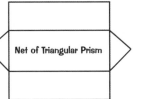
Net of Triangular Prism

Cube

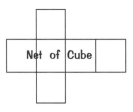
Net of Cube

5) The <u>SURFACE AREAS OF SPHERES, CYLINDERS AND CONES</u> are particularly important (because they're mentioned in the specification).

SPHERES:
Surface area = 4πr²

CONES:
Surface area = πrl + πr²

curved area of cone   area of circular base

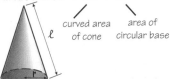

CYLINDERS:
Surface area = 2πrh + 2πr²

Especially note that <u>the length of the rectangle</u> is equal to the <u>circumference of the circular ends.</u>

Cylinder

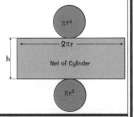
Net of Cylinder

The Acid Test:

LEARN the <u>Rules for Identifying Formulas</u>, and the <u>5 Points for Surface Area and Nets.</u>

1) Identify these expressions as an area, volume, or perimeter:
  a) 2bh+4lp, b) 4r²p+3πd³, c) (4πr²+dh)/d   2) Draw the net of a cone.
3) Work out the surface area of a cylindrical drink can of height 12.5cm and diameter 7.2cm.

Circle Geometry

9 Simple Rules — That's all:

1) ANGLE IN A SEMICIRCLE = 90⁰

A triangle drawn from the two ends of a diameter will ALWAYS make an angle of 90° where it meets the edge of the circle.

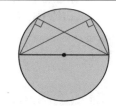

2) TANGENT and RADIUS MEET AT 90⁰

A TANGENT is a line that just touches the edge of a circle or other curve. If a tangent and radius meet at the same point, then the angle they make is EXACTLY 90°.

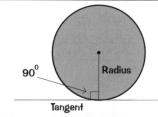

3) SNEAKY ISOSCELES TRIANGLES FORMED BY TWO RADII

Unlike other isosceles triangles they don't have the little tick marks on the sides to remind you that they are the same — the fact that they are both radii is enough to make it an isosceles triangle.

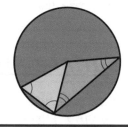

4) CHORD BISECTOR IS A DIAMETER

A CHORD is any line drawn across a circle. And no matter where you draw a chord, the line that cuts it exactly in half (at 90°), will go through the centre of the circle and so will be a DIAMETER.

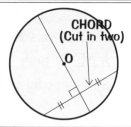

5) ANGLES IN THE SAME SEGMENT ARE EQUAL

All triangles drawn from a chord will have the same angle where they touch the circle. Also, the two angles on opposite sides of the chord add up to 180°.

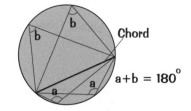

6) ANGLE AT THE CENTRE IS TWICE THE ANGLE AT THE EDGE

The angle subtended at the centre of a circle is EXACTLY DOUBLE the angle subtended at the edge of the circle from the same two points (two ends of the same chord). The phrase "angle subtended at" is nothing complicated, it's just a bit posher than saying "angle made at".

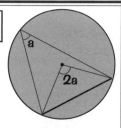

7) OPPOSITE ANGLES OF A CYCLIC QUADRILATERAL ADD UP TO 180⁰

$a+c=180^0$

$b+d=180^0$

A *cyclic quadrilateral* is a 4-sided shape with every corner touching the circle. Both pairs of opposite angles add up to 180°.

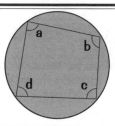

Circle Geometry

8) EQUALITY OF TANGENTS FROM A POINT

The two tangents drawn from an outside point are <u>always equal in length</u>, so creating an "isosceles" situation, with <u>two congruent right-angled triangles</u> *(if you don't know what congruent means, see p77).*

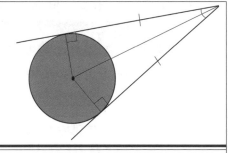

9) ANGLE IN OPPOSITE SEGMENT IS EQUAL

This is perhaps the trickiest one to remember. If you draw a <u>tangent</u> and a <u>chord</u> that meet, then <u>the angle between them</u> is always <u>equal</u> to *"the angle in the opposite segment"* (i.e. the angle made at the edge of the circle by two lines drawn from the chord).

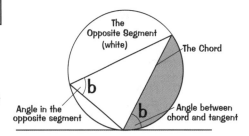

3-Letter Notation for Angles

1) <u>Angles are specified using 3 letters</u>, e.g. angle ODC = 48°
2) <u>THE MIDDLE LETTER IS WHERE THE ANGLE IS</u>
3) <u>THE OTHER TWO LETTERS</u> tell you <u>which lines enclose the angle</u>
   For example: Angle ODC is <u>at D</u> and
   <u>enclosed by the lines</u> going from <u>O to D</u> and from <u>D to C</u>.

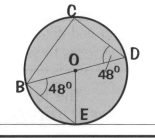

An Example

"Find all the angles in this diagram."

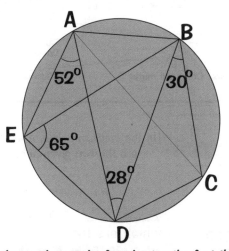

ANSWER:

1) ANGLE IN SAME SEGMENT
EAD = EBD = 52°
ADB = AEB = ACB = 28°
DBC = DAC = 30°
DEB = DAB = 65° ⇒ BAC = (65° − 30°) = 35°

2) OPPOSITE ANGLES of a CYCLIC QUADRILATERAL ADD UP TO 180°
<u>Quadrilateral ABDE:</u>
BDE = 180° − (30° + 52° + 35°) = 63°
⇒ ADE = 63° − 28° = 35°
ABD = 180° − (65° + 28°) = 87°
⇒ ABE = 87° − 52° = 35°
<u>Quadrilateral ABCD:</u>
BCD = 180° − (30° + 35°) = 115°
⇒ ACD = 115° − 28° = 87°
ADC = 180° − (30° + 35° + 52°) = 63°
⇒ BCD = 63° − 28° = 35°

All other angles can be found using the fact that the <u>angles of a triangle and along a straight line add up to 180°</u>.

The Acid Test:

LEARN all <u>Nine Rules</u> on these two pages.
Then <u>turn over and write them all down</u>.

1) Find all the angles in the 3rd diagram above illustrating the 3-letter notation (ODC = 48°, etc.).
2) <u>Practise the above Example</u> till you <u>understand every step</u> and can do it easily without help.

Loci and Constructions

A <u>LOCUS</u> (another ridiculous maths word) is simply:

> ## A LINE that shows <u>all the points which fit in with a given rule.</u>

Make sure you <u>learn</u> how to do these <u>PROPERLY</u> using a <u>RULER AND COMPASSES</u> as shown on these two pages.

1) The locus of points which are <u>"A FIXED DISTANCE from a given POINT"</u>

This locus is simply a <u>CIRCLE</u>.

Pair of Compasses

A given point

The LOCUS of points equidistant from it

2) The locus of points which are <u>"A FIXED DISTANCE from a given LINE"</u>

This locus is an <u>OVAL SHAPE</u>

It has <u>straight sides</u> (drawn with a <u>ruler</u>) and <u>ends</u> which are <u>perfect semicircles</u> (drawn with <u>compasses</u>).

Semicircle ends drawn with compasses

A given line

The LOCUS of points equidistant from it

3) The locus of points which are <u>"EQUIDISTANT from TWO GIVEN LINES"</u>

1) Keep the compass setting <u>THE SAME</u> while you make <u>all four marks</u>.

2) Make sure you <u>leave</u> your compass marks <u>showing</u>.

3) You get <u>two equal angles</u> — i.e. this <u>LOCUS</u> is actually an <u>ANGLE BISECTOR</u>.

Step 1

Step 2

A given line

The LOCUS

Second Compass marks

First Compass marks

The other given line

4) The locus of points which are <u>"EQUIDISTANT from TWO GIVEN POINTS"</u>

(In the diagram below, A and B are the two given points.)

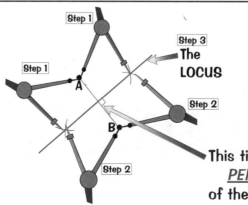

Step 1

Step 1

Step 3
The LOCUS

Step 2

A

B

Step 2

<u>This LOCUS</u> is all points which are the <u>same distance</u> from A as they are from B.

This time the locus is actually the <u>PERPENDICULAR BISECTOR</u> of the line joining the two points.

Loci and Constructions

Constructing accurate 60° angles

1) They may well ask you to draw an _accurate 60° angle_.

2) One place they're needed is for drawing an _equilateral triangle_.

3) Make sure you _follow the method_ shown in this diagram, and that you can do it _entirely from memory_.

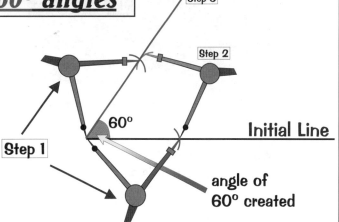

Step 3

Step 2

Step 1

60°

Initial Line

angle of 60° created

Constructing accurate 90° angles

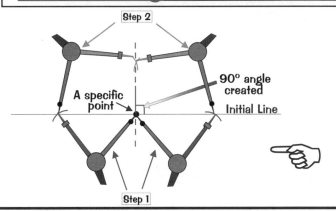

Step 2

Step 1

A specific point

90° angle created

Initial Line

1) They might want you to draw an _accurate 90° angle_.

2) They won't accept it just done "_by eye_" or with a ruler — if you want the marks you've got to do it _the proper way_ with _compasses_ like I've shown you here.

3) Make sure you can _follow the method_ shown in this diagram.

Drawing the Perpendicular from a Point to a Line

1) This is similar to the one above but _not quite the same_ — make sure you can do _both_.

2) Again, they won't accept it just done "_by eye_" or with a ruler — you've got to do it _the proper way_ with _compasses_.

3) _Learn_ the diagram.

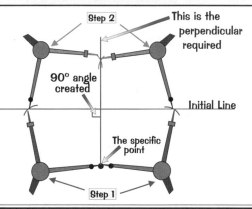

Step 2

This is the perpendicular required

90° angle created

Initial Line

The specific point

Step 1

The Acid Test: LEARN EVERYTHING ON THESE TWO PAGES.

Now cover up these two pages and draw an example of each of the four loci.

Also draw an equilateral triangle and a square, both with fabulously accurate 60° and 90° angles.

Also, draw a line and a point and construct the perpendicular from the point to the line.

The Four Transformations

Transformations are about the most fun you can have without laughing.

Translation	—	ONE Detail
Enlargement	—	TWO Details
Rotation	—	THREE Details
Reflection	—	ONE Detail
Y		

1) Use the word _TERRY_ to remember the 4 types.

2) You must always remember to specify _all the details_ for each type.

1) TRANSLATION

You must specify this ONE detail:	1) the VECTOR OF TRANSLATION (See P.79 on vector notation)

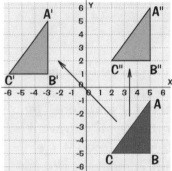

ABC to A'B'C' is a _translation of_ $\begin{pmatrix} -8 \\ 6 \end{pmatrix}$

ABC to A"B"C" is a _translation of_ $\begin{pmatrix} 0 \\ 7 \end{pmatrix}$

2) ENLARGEMENT

You must specify these 2 details:	1) The SCALE FACTOR 2) The CENTRE of Enlargement

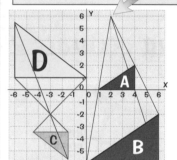

A to B is an enlargement of _scale factor 2_, and _centre (2,6)_

B to A is an enlargement of _scale factor 1/2_ and _centre (2,6)_

C to D is an enlargement of _scale factor -2_ and _centre (-3,-2)_

3) ROTATION

You must specify these 3 details:	1) ANGLE turned 2) DIRECTION (Clockwise or..) 3) CENTRE of Rotation

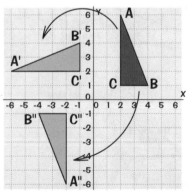

ABC to A'B'C' is a Rotation of $90°$, _anticlockwise_, ABOUT the origin.

ABC to A"B"C" is a Rotation of _half a turn (180°)_, _clockwise_, ABOUT the origin.

4) REFLECTION

You must specify this ONE detail:	1) The MIRROR LINE

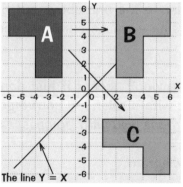

The line Y = X

A to B is a _reflection IN the Y-axis._

A to C is a _reflection IN the line Y=X_

The Acid Test:

LEARN the names of the Four Transformations and the details that go with each. When you think you know it, turn over and write it all down.

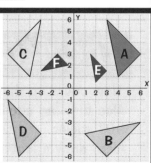

1) Describe _fully_ these transformations: A → B,   E → A,   F → B,
   B → C,   C → A,   A → D,   A → E,   B → F.

Congruence and Similarity

Congruence is another ridiculous maths word which sounds really complicated when it's not: If two shapes are <u>CONGRUENT</u>, they are simply <u>the same</u> — <u>the same size and the same shape</u>. That's all it is. They can however be <u>MIRROR IMAGES</u>.

<u>CONGRUENT</u>
— same size, same shape

<u>SIMILAR</u>
— same shape, <u>different size</u>

Note that the angles are always unchanged.

Congruent Triangles — are they or aren't they?

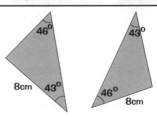

Probably the <u>trickiest area</u> of congruence is deciding whether <u>two triangles</u>, like the ones shown here, are CONGRUENT.

In other words, from the skimpy information given, are the two going to be the same or different.
There are <u>THREE IMPORTANT STEPS</u>:

1) The Golden Rule is definitely to DRAW THEM BOTH IN THE SAME ORIENTATION
— only then can you compare them properly:

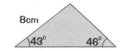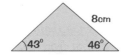

2) <u>Don't jump to hasty conclusions</u> — although the 8cm sides are clearly in different positions, it's always possible that <u>both top sides are 8cm</u>.

In this case we can work out that they're <u>not</u> because the angles are different (so they can't be isosceles).

3) <u>Now see if any of these conditions are true.</u> If <u>ONE</u> of the conditions holds, the triangles are <u>congruent</u>.

1) SSS	*three sides are the same*	
2) AAS	*two angles and a side match up*	
3) SAS	*two sides and the angle between them match up*	
4) RHS	*a right angle, the hypotenuse (longest side) and one other side all match up*	

For two triangles to be congruent, ONE OR MORE of these four conditions must be true.
(If none are true, then you have proof that the triangles aren't congruent.)

Similar Shapes And the Formula Triangle

The lengths of two <u>SIMILAR SHAPES</u> are related to the Scale Factor by this <u>VERY important Formula Triangle WHICH YOU MUST LEARN</u>:

This enables you to tackle <u>the classic "Enlarged photo" Exam question</u> with breathtaking triviality: (See P.49 for how to use formula triangles)

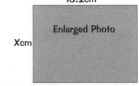

To find the width of the enlarged photo we <u>use the formula triangle twice</u>, first to find the <u>Scale Factor</u>, and then to find the <u>missing side</u>:

1) Scale Factor = New length÷Old length = 13.2÷8.4 = <u>1.57</u>
2) New width = Scale Factor × Old width = 1.57×5.8 = <u>9.1cm</u>

<u>WITHOUT THE FORMULA TRIANGLE THIS CAN PROVE QUITE TRICKY</u>

The Acid Test:

LEARN the definitions of <u>similarity and congruence</u>, the <u>rules</u> for checking for <u>congruent triangles</u>, and the use of the <u>FORMULA TRIANGLE</u> for Similar Shapes.

Then, *when you think you know it*, turn the page over and *write it all down again*, from *memory*, including the sketches and examples, *especially the photo enlargement* one.

Similarity and Enlargements

4 Key Features

1) If the <u>Scale Factor is bigger than 1</u> the <u>shape gets bigger</u>.

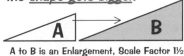

A to B is an Enlargement, Scale Factor 1½

2) If the <u>Scale Factor is smaller than 1</u> (i.e. a fraction like ½) then the <u>shape gets smaller</u>. (Really this is a reduction, but you still call it <u>an Enlargement, Scale Factor ½</u>)

A to B is an Enlargement of Scale Factor ½

3) If the <u>Scale Factor is NEGATIVE</u> then the shape pops out the other side of the enlargement centre. If the scale factor is -1, it's exactly the same as a rotation of 180^0.

A to B is an enlargement of scale factor -2. B to A is an enlargement of scale factor -½.

4) The <u>Scale Factor</u> also tells you the <u>relative distance</u> of old points and new points <u>from the Centre of Enlargement</u> — this is <u>very useful for drawing an enlargement</u>, because you can use it to trace out the positions of the new points:

Scale factor 3:

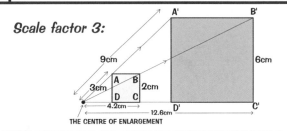

THE CENTRE OF ENLARGEMENT

Areas and Volumes of Enlargements

Ho ho! This little joker catches everybody out. The increase in area and volume is <u>BIGGER</u> than the scale factor.

    <u>For example</u>, if the <u>Scale Factor is 2</u>, the lengths are <u>twice as big</u>, each area is <u>4 times</u> as big, and the volume is <u>8 times</u> as big. The rule is below:

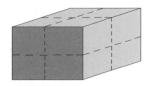

<u>For a Scale Factor n</u>:

The <u>SIDES</u> are	n times bigger
The <u>AREAS</u> are	n^2 times bigger
The <u>VOLUMES</u> are	n^3 times bigger

    Simple... but <u>VERY FORGETTABLE</u>

These ratios can also be expressed in this form:

Lengths	$n : m$	e.g. $3 : 4$
Areas	$n^2 : m^2$	e.g. $9 : 16$
Volumes	$n^3 : m^3$	e.g. $27 : 64$

<u>A PARTICULAR EXAMPLE</u>: 2 spheres have surface areas of $16m^2$ and $25m^2$. Find the ratio of their volumes. (This conversion <u>from area ratio to volume ratio</u> is specifically mentioned in the specification. Make sure you can do it.)

<u>ANS</u>: $16 : 25$ is the areas ratio which must be $n^2 : m^2$, i.e. $n^2 : m^2 = 16 : 25$
and so $n : m = 4 : 5$
and so $n^3 : m^3 = \underline{64 : 125}$ = the ratio of their volumes

The Acid Test:
<u>LEARN</u> the <u>4 Key Features</u> for Enlargements, plus the <u>3 Rules for Area and Volume Ratios</u>. Then <u>turn over and write them all down</u>.

1) Draw the triangle A(2,1) B(5,2) C(4,4) and enlarge it by a scale factor of -1½, centred on the origin. Label the new triangle A' B' C' and give the coordinates of its corners.

2) Two similar cones have volumes of $27m^3$ and $64m^3$. If the surface area of the smaller one is $36m^2$, find the surface area of the other one.

Vectors

4 MONSTROUSLY IMPORTANT THINGS you need to know about *Vectors*:

1) *The Four Notations*

The vector shown here can be referred to as

or $\underline{a}$ or **a** (in bold type) or $\overrightarrow{AB}$

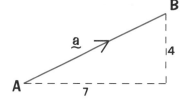

It's pretty obvious what these mean. Just make sure you know which is which in the column vector (x→ and y↑) and what a negative value means in a column vector.

2) *Adding And Subtracting Vectors*

Vectors must always be added END TO END, so that the *arrows all point WITH each other*, not AGAINST each other.

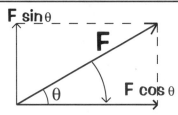

Adding and subtracting COLUMN VECTORS is really easy: E.g. if $\underline{a} = \begin{pmatrix} 5 \\ 3 \end{pmatrix}$ and $\underline{b} = \begin{pmatrix} -2 \\ 4 \end{pmatrix}$ then $2\underline{a} - \underline{b} = 2\begin{pmatrix} 5 \\ 3 \end{pmatrix} - \begin{pmatrix} -2 \\ 4 \end{pmatrix} = \begin{pmatrix} 12 \\ 2 \end{pmatrix}$

3) *Splitting Into Components*

Any vector can be split into two components that are at $90°$ to each other. These two components will always be $F\cos\theta$ *and* $F\sin\theta$. The main difficulty is knowing which one is which. *Learn this:*

When you turn F through angle θ as shown, you get $F\cos\theta$ (So the other one must be $F\sin\theta$)

4) *A Typical Exam Question*

This is a common type of question and it illustrates a very important vector technique:

To obtain the *unknown vector* just *'get there'* by any route *made up of known vectors*.

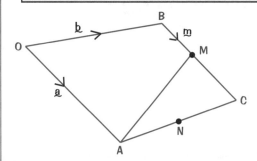

Applying this rule we can easily obtain the following vectors in term of $\underline{a}$, $\underline{b}$ and $\underline{m}$, (given that M and N are mid points):

1) $\overrightarrow{AM} = -\underline{a} + \underline{b} + \underline{m}$ (i.e. get there via O and B)

2) $\overrightarrow{OC} = \underline{b} + 2\underline{m}$ (i.e. get there via B and M)

3) $\overrightarrow{AC} = -\underline{a} + \underline{b} + 2\underline{m}$ (A to C via O, B and M)

The Acid Test:

LEARN the important details on this page, then *turn over and write them down*.

1) For the diagram above express the following in terms of $\underline{a}$, $\underline{b}$ and $\underline{m}$:

   a) $\overrightarrow{MO}$ b) $\overrightarrow{AN}$ c) $\overrightarrow{BN}$ d) $\overrightarrow{NM}$

"Real-Life" Vector Questions

These are the type of vector question you're most likely to get in the Exam, so make sure you learn all the little tricks on this page.

1) The Old "Swimming Across the River" Question

This is a really easy question: You just _ADD the two velocity vectors END TO END_ and draw the _RESULTANT vector_ which shows both the _speed and direction of the final course_. Simple huh?

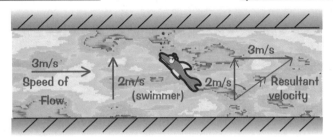

Overall Speed =
$$\sqrt{3^2 + 2^2} = \sqrt{13} = \underline{3.6 m/s}$$
Direction: $TAN \theta = 3 \div 2$
$$\theta = TAN^{-1} (1.5) = \underline{56.3^0}$$

As usual with vectors, you'll need to use _Pythagoras and Trig_ to find the length and angle but that's no big deal is it? Just make sure you **LEARN** the two methods in this question.

The example shown above is absolutely bog-standard stuff and you should definitely see it that way, rather than as one random question of which there may be hundreds — there aren't!

2) The Old "Swimming Slightly Upstream" Question

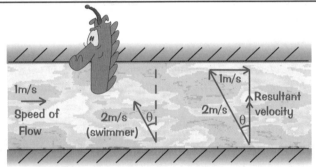

1) $SIN \theta = OPP/HYP$
$$= 1/2$$
so $\theta = SIN^{-1} (0.5) = \underline{30^0}$

2) $\underline{Speed} = \sqrt{2^2 - 1^2} = \sqrt{3} =$
$$\underline{1.73 \ m/s}$$

The general idea here is to _end up going directly across the river_, and _ONCE AGAIN the old faithful method_ of _DRAWING A VECTOR TRIANGLE_ makes light work of the whole thing — 2 vectors joined _END TO END_ to give the resultant velocity. However, in this case the resultant is drawn in FIRST (straight across), so that _the angle θ has to be worked out to fit_ as shown above.

3) The Old "Queen Mary's Tugboats" Question

The problem here is to find the overall force from the two tugs.

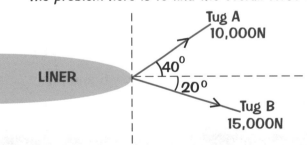

This can be tackled in two ways:
1) By working out the <u>COMPONENTS of the two force vectors</u> along both dotted lines (F COS θ and F SIN θ etc.)
<u>OR</u>:
2) By <u>adding the vectors END TO END</u> to make a vector triangle and using the <u>SINE & COSINE RULES</u> (See P.87).

The Acid Test:
LEARN the 3 EXAMPLES on this page, then <u>turn over and write them out</u>, but with <u>different numbers</u>.

1) Work out the overall force on the Queen Mary in example 3, using <u>BOTH</u> methods.

Pythagoras' Theorem and Bearings

Pythagoras' Theorem — $a^2 + b^2 = h^2$

1) _PYTHAGORAS' THEOREM_ always goes hand in hand with SIN, COS and TAN because they're all involved with _RIGHT-ANGLED TRIANGLES_.

2) The big difference is that _PYTHAGORAS DOES NOT INVOLVE ANY ANGLES_ — it just uses _two sides_ to find the _third side_. (SIN, COS and TAN always involve _ANGLES_)

3) _THE BASIC FORMULA_ for Pythagoras is $a^2 + b^2 = h^2$

4) _PLUG THE NUMBERS IN_ and work it out.

5) _BUT GET THE NUMBERS IN THE RIGHT PLACE_. The 2 shorter sides squared add to equal the longest side squared.

6) _ALWAYS CHECK THAT YOUR ANSWER IS SENSIBLE_.

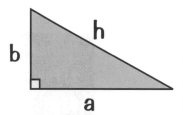

Example

"Find the missing side in the triangle shown."

ANSWER:

$a^2 + b^2 = h^2$ $\therefore x^2 = 25 - 9 = 16$

$\therefore 3^2 + x^2 = 5^2$ $\therefore x = \sqrt{16} = \underline{4m}$

$\therefore 9 + x^2 = 25$ (Is it _sensible_? — Yes, it's shorter than 5m, but not too much shorter)

Bearings

To find or plot a bearing you must remember _the three key words_:

1) "FROM"

Find the word "FROM" in the question, and put your pencil on the diagram at the point you are going _"from"_.

2) NORTH LINE

At the point you are going _FROM_, _draw in a NORTH LINE_.

3) CLOCKWISE

Now draw in the angle CLOCKWISE _from the north line to the line joining the two points_. This angle is the required bearing.

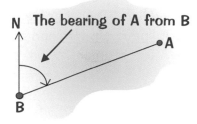

The bearing of A from B

Example

"Find the bearing of Q _from P_":

2) _North line_ at P

1) _"From_ P"

3) _Clockwise_, from the N-line. This angle is the _bearing of Q from P_ and is _245°_.

N.B. _All bearings should be given as 3 figures_, e.g. 176°, 034° (not 34°), 005° (not 5°), 018° etc.

The Acid Test:

LEARN the _6 facts about Pythagoras_ and the _3 key words for bearings_. Then _turn over and write them down_.

1) Find the length of BC.
2) Find the bearing of T from H, by measuring from the diagram with a protractor.
3) CALCULATE the bearing of H from T.

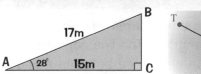

Pythagoras, Lines and Line Segments

Use Pythagoras to find the Distance Between Points

Now you've got the hang of <u>Pythagoras' Theorem</u>, you need to know <u>when to apply it</u>.
In the Exam you'll have to spot when to use it for yourself.

Example: *"Point P has coordinates (8, 3) and point Q has coordinates (-4, 8). Find the length of the line segment PQ."*

If you get a question like this, follow these rules and it'll all become breathtakingly simple:

> 1) Draw a <u>sketch</u> to find the <u>right-angled triangle</u>.
>
> 2) Find the <u>lengths of the sides</u> of the triangle.
>
> 3) <u>Use Pythagoras</u> to find the <u>length of the diagonal</u>.
>   (That's your answer.)

Solution: ①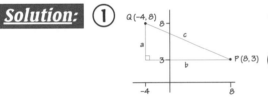

② Length of <u>side a</u> = 8 – 3 = 5
   Length of <u>side b</u> = 8 – -4 = 12

③ <u>Use Pythagoras</u> to find <u>side c</u>:
   $c^2 = a^2 + b^2 = 5^2 + 12^2 = 25 + 144 = 169$
   So: $c = \sqrt{169} = 13$

A Line Segment is Part of a Line...

1) The example above asked you to find the length of the line PQ. To be really precise, the line PQ <u>isn't actually a line</u> — it's a **LINE SEGMENT**. Confused, read on...

2) A <u>line</u> is <u>straight</u> and continues <u>to infinity</u> (it goes on forever) in both directions. A <u>line segment</u> is just <u>part</u> of a line — it has 2 end points.

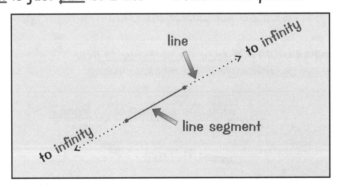

3) So the length PQ is just a <u>chunk</u> of the line running through P and Q. <u>Don't worry too much</u> about lines and line segments. The specification says you need to know the difference — and now you do. Just be aware that things which are actually line segments will often be referred to as lines.

The Acid Test:
LEARN the details on this page, then <u>turn over and write them down.</u>

1) Point A has coordinates (10, 15) and point B has coordinates (6, 12).
   Find the length of the line segment AB.
2) What is the difference between a line and a line segment?

Trigonometry — SIN, COS, TAN

There are several methods for doing Trig and they're all pretty much the same. However, _the method shown below has a number of advantages_, mainly because the _formula triangles_ mean the same method is used every time (no matter which side or angle is being asked for). _This makes the whole topic a lot simpler_, and you'll find that once you've learned this method, the answers automatically come out right every time. It's just a joy.

Method

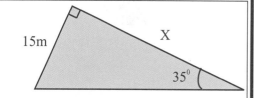

1) **Label the three sides O, A and H**
   (Opposite, Adjacent and Hypotenuse).

2) **Write down FROM MEMORY "SOH CAH TOA"**
   (Sounds like a Chinese word, "Sockatoa!")

3) **Decide WHICH TWO SIDES are INVOLVED O,H A,H or O,A**
   and select <u>S</u>OH, <u>C</u>AH or <u>T</u>OA accordingly.

4) **Turn the one you choose into a FORMULA TRIANGLE:**

5) **Cover up the thing you want to find** (with your finger),
   and write down whatever is left showing.

6) **Translate into numbers and work it out.**

7) **Finally, check that your answer is SENSIBLE.**

Some Nitty Gritty Details

1) The <u>Hypotenuse</u> is the <u>LONGEST SIDE</u>. The <u>Opposite</u> is the side <u>OPPOSITE</u> the angle <u>being used</u> (θ), and the <u>Adjacent</u> is the side <u>NEXT TO</u> the angle <u>being used</u>.

2) In the formula triangles, S^θ represents SIN θ, C^θ is COS θ, and T^θ is TAN θ.

3) Remember, <u>TO FIND THE ANGLE — USE INVERSE</u>, i.e. press [INV] or [SHIFT] or [2nd], followed by SIN, COS or TAN (and make sure your calculator is in DEG mode).

4) You can only use SIN, COS and TAN on <u>RIGHT-ANGLED TRIANGLES</u> — you may have to add lines to the diagram to create one, especially with _isosceles triangles_.

The Acid Test:
LEARN the <u>7 Steps of the Method</u> and the Four Nitty Gritty Details. Then turn over and write them down.

Practising past paper questions is very important, but the whole point of doing so is to check and consolidate the methods <u>you have already learnt</u>. Don't make the mistake of thinking it's pointless learning these 7 steps. <u>If you don't know them all thoroughly, you'll just keep on getting questions wrong</u>.

Trigonometry — SIN, COS, TAN

Example 1) "Find x in the triangle shown."

1) Label O,A,H
2) Write down "SOH CAH TOA"
3) Two sides _involved_: O,H

4) So use

5) We want to find H so cover it up to leave: $H = \frac{O}{S^\theta}$

6) Translate :  $X = \frac{15}{SIN\ 35}$

Press [15] [÷] [SIN] [35] [=]   [26.151702]   So ans = **26.2m**

7) Check it's sensible: yes — it's about twice as big as 15.

(N.B. on some calculators you press [35] [SIN] rather than [SIN] [35] — Know yours!)

Triangle labels: **Hyp** x, **Opp** 15m, **Adj**, angle 35°

Example 2) "Find the angle θ in this triangle."

1) Label O, A, H
2) Write down "SOH CAH TOA'"
3) Two sides _involved_: A,H

4) So use

5) We want to find θ so cover up C^θ to leave: $C^\theta = \frac{A}{H}$

6) Translate: $COS\ \theta = \frac{15}{25} = 0.6$

NOW USE INVERSE :   θ = INV COS (0.6)

Press [INV] [COS] [0.6] [=]   [53.130102]   So ans = **53.1°**

7) Finally, is it sensible? — Yes.

Triangle: 25m, 25m sides, 30m base, angle θ

Note the usual way of dealing with an _ISOSCELES TRIANGLE_: split it _down the middle_ to get a _RIGHT ANGLE_:

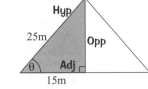

Right triangle labels: **Hyp** 25m, **Opp**, angle θ, **Adj**, 15m

---

Angles of Elevation and Depression

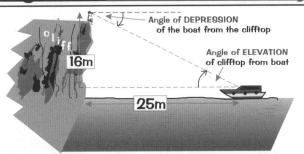

Angle of DEPRESSION of the boat from the clifftop
Angle of ELEVATION of clifftop from boat
cliff, 16m, 25m

1) The _Angle of Depression_ is the angle _downwards_ from the horizontal.

2) The _Angle of Elevation_ is the angle _upwards_ from the horizontal.

3) The Angles of Elevation and Depression are _EQUAL_.

The Acid Test: Practise these two questions until you can apply the method _fluently_ and without having to refer to it _at all_.

1) Find X: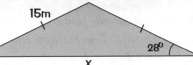
   15m, 28°, x

2) Find θ: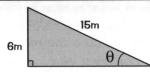
   15m, 6m, θ

3) Calculate the angles of elevation and depression in the boat drawing above.

Pythagoras and Trigonometry in 3D

3D questions on Pythagoras and trig might seem a bit mind-boggling
at first — but you're really just using those same old rules.

Angle Between Line and Plane — Use a Diagram

Learn The 3-Step Method

1) Make a __RIGHT-ANGLED__ triangle using __the line__, __a line in
the plane__ and __a line between the two__.

2) __Draw__ this right-angled triangle again so that you can
see it __clearly__. __Label__ the sides. You might have to use
__Pythagoras__ to work out the length of one of the sides.

3) Use __trigonometry__ to calculate the angle.

Example: *"ABCDE is a square-based pyramid. It is 12 cm high and the square base has sides of length 7 cm. Find the angle the edge AE makes with the base."*

X is the centre
of the square
base.

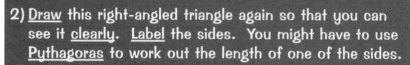

1) First draw a __right-angled triangle__ using the __edge AE__, the __base__ and __a line between
the two__ (in this case the central height). Call the angle you're trying to find __θ__.

2) Now draw this triangle __clearly__ and label it.

To find θ, you need to know the length of side **EX**.

So, using __Pythagoras__ — $EX^2 = 3.5^2 + 3.5^2 = 24.5 \Rightarrow EX = \sqrt{24.5}$ cm

You know the lengths of the
__opposite__ and __adjacent__
sides, so use __tan__.

3) Now use __trigonometry__ to find the angle θ:

$$\tan\theta = \frac{12}{\sqrt{24.5}} = 2.4... \qquad \theta = \underline{67.6°} \text{ (1 d.p.)}$$

Use Right-Angled Triangles To Find Lengths too

Example: *"ABCDEFGH is a cube with sides of 3 cm. Find the length of BH."*

1) First use __Pythagoras__ to find the length __FH__.

$$FH^2 = 3^2 + 3^2 = 18 \Rightarrow FH = \sqrt{18} \text{ cm}$$

2) Now use __Pythagoras__ again to find the length __BH__.

$$BH^2 = 3^2 + (\sqrt{18})^2 = 27 \Rightarrow BH = \sqrt{27} \text{ cm} = \underline{5.2 \text{ cm}} \text{ (1 decimal place)}$$

The Acid Test:

1) Calculate the angle that line AG makes with the base of this cuboid.
2) Calculate the length of AG.

The Sine and Cosine Rules

Normal trigonometry using SOH CAH TOA etc. <u>can only be applied to right-angled triangles</u>. <u>The Sine and Cosine Rules</u> on the other hand allow you to tackle <u>any triangle at all</u> with <u>contemptuous ease</u>.

Labelling The Triangle

This is very important. You must label the sides and angles properly so that the letters for the sides and angles correspond with each other:

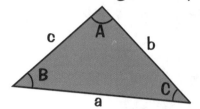

Remember, *side "a" is opposite angle A* etc.

It doesn't matter which sides you decide to call a, b, and c, just as long as the angles are then labelled properly.

Three Formulas to Learn:

They're quite an odd-looking set of formulas really, but don't be put off by that. Once you know how to operate them they're just like any other formula — stick the numbers in, crank the handle and out pops the answer.

The Sine Rule

You don't use the whole thing with both "=" signs of course, so it's not half as bad as it looks — you just choose the two bits that you want:

$$\frac{a}{\text{SIN A}} = \frac{b}{\text{SIN B}} = \frac{c}{\text{SIN C}}$$

e.g. $\dfrac{b}{\text{SIN B}} = \dfrac{c}{\text{SIN C}}$ or $\dfrac{a}{\text{SIN A}} = \dfrac{b}{\text{SIN B}}$

The Cosine Rule

$$a^2 = b^2 + c^2 - 2bc\,\text{COS A}$$

or $\text{COS A} = \dfrac{b^2 + c^2 - a^2}{2\,bc}$

You should LEARN these three formulas off by heart. If you can't, you won't be able to use them successfully in the Exam, even if they give them to you.

When Do You Use Which Rule?

1) Basically, <u>THE SINE RULE</u> is *much simpler* so always try to use it first <u>IF POSSIBLE</u>.
2) However, *you don't usually have a lot of choice*.

The good news is that there are only FOUR basic questions, <u>TWO</u> which need the <u>SINE RULE</u> and <u>TWO</u> which need the <u>COSINE RULE</u> as detailed on the next page. However, once you know <u>4 BITS OF DATA</u> (e.g. 2 sides and 2 angles, or 3 sides and 1 angle) then the rest is easily worked out (with the SINE RULE preferably).

The Acid Test:

LEARN the <u>proper labelling</u>, the <u>Three Formulas</u>, and <u>how to decide which rule to use</u>.

Now <u>turn over and write down everything on this page</u>.

The Sine and Cosine Rules

The Four Examples

Amazingly enough there are <u>BASICALLY ONLY FOUR</u> questions where the SINE and COSINE rules would be applied. _Learn the exact details of these four basic examples:_

1) <u>TWO ANGLES given plus ANY SIDE:</u>

— SINE RULE NEEDED

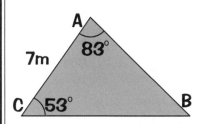

1) Don't forget the obvious: $B = 180 - 83 - 53 = \underline{44^0}$

2) Then use $\dfrac{b}{SIN\ B} = \dfrac{c}{SIN\ C} \Rightarrow \dfrac{7}{SIN\ 44} = \dfrac{c}{SIN\ 53}$

3) Which gives $\Rightarrow c = \dfrac{7 \times SIN\ 53}{SIN\ 44} = \underline{8.05m}$

The rest is easy using the SINE RULE.

2) <u>TWO SIDES given plus an ANGLE NOT ENCLOSED by them:</u>

— SINE RULE NEEDED

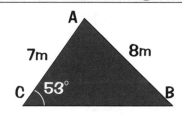

$\dfrac{b}{SIN\ B} = \dfrac{c}{SIN\ C} \Rightarrow \dfrac{7}{SIN\ B} = \dfrac{8}{SIN\ 53}$

$\Rightarrow SIN\ B = \dfrac{7 \times SIN\ 53}{8} = 0.6988 \Rightarrow B = SIN^{-1}(0.6988) = 44.3^\circ$

The rest is easy using the SINE RULE.

3) <u>TWO SIDES given plus THE ANGLE ENCLOSED by them:</u>

— COSINE RULE NEEDED

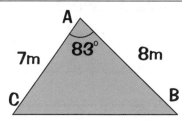

Use: $a^2 = b^2 + c^2 - 2bc\,COS\ A$

$= 7^2 + 8^2 - 2 \times 7 \times 8 \times COS\ 83$

$= 99.3506 \Rightarrow a = \sqrt{99.3506} = \underline{9.97}$

The rest is easy using the SINE RULE.

4) <u>ALL THREE SIDES given but NO ANGLES:</u>

— COSINE RULE NEEDED

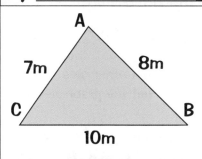

1) Use $COS\ A = \dfrac{b^2 + c^2 - a^2}{2bc}$

$= \dfrac{49 + 64 - 100}{2 \times 7 \times 8} = \dfrac{13}{112} = 0.11607$

2) Hence $A = COS^{-1}(0.11607) = \underline{83.3^0}$

The rest is easy using the SINE RULE.

The Acid Test:

LEARN the <u>FOUR BASIC TYPES</u> as above.
Then cover the page and do these:

1) Write down _a new version_ of each of the 4 examples above and then use the SINE and COSINE RULES to find <u>ALL of the sides and angles</u> for each one.

2) A triangle has two sides of 12m and 17m with an angle of 70^0 between them. Find all the other sides and angles in the triangle. (A sketch is essential, of course).

The Graphs of SIN, COS and TAN

You are expected to know these graphs and be able to SKETCH them from memory. It really isn't that difficult — the secret is to notice their SIMILARITIES and DIFFERENCES:

Y = SIN X

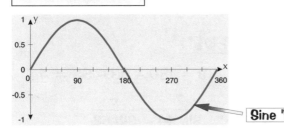

Sine 'Wave'

Y = COS X

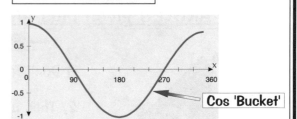

Cos 'Bucket'

1) <u>For 0° – 360°</u>, the shapes you get are a <u>SINE "WAVE"</u> (one peak, one trough) and a <u>COS "BUCKET"</u> (*Starts at the top, dips, and finishes at the top*).

2) The *underlying shape* of both the SIN and COS graphs are *identical*, (as shown below) when you extend them (indefinitely) in both directions:

Y = SIN X

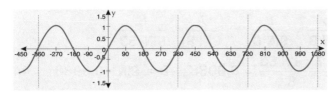

Y = COS X

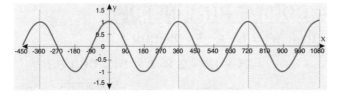

3) The only difference is that the SIN graph is shifted by 90° → compared to the COS graph.

4) Note that <u>BOTH GRAPHS</u> wiggle between *y-limits of exactly +1 and -1.*

5) *The key to drawing the extended graphs* is to first draw the 0 – 360° cycle of either the <u>SIN "WAVE"</u> or the <u>COS "BUCKET"</u> and then *repeat it in both directions as shown*.

Y = TAN X

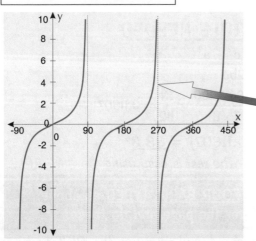

1) <u>The TAN graph BEARS NO RESEMBLANCE to the other two.</u>

2) *It behaves in a fairly bizarre way at 90°, 270° etc.* ....by disappearing up to *+ infinity* and then reappearing from *- infinity* on the other side of the *asymptote* (— a dotted line that the graph never quite touches).

3) *So unlike the SIN and COS graphs*, Y = TAN X is <u>NOT LIMITED *to values between +1 and -1*.</u>

4) You'll also notice that whilst SIN and COS repeat *every 360°*, the TAN graph *repeats every 180°*.

The Acid Test:
LEARN The <u>FIVE</u> graphs above. <u>Then turn over and draw all five again in full detail.</u>

Angles of Any Size

YOU CAN ONLY DO THIS IF YOU'VE LEARNT THE GRAPHS ON THE OTHER PAGE.

SIN, COS and TAN for Angles of Any Size

There is ONE BASIC IDEA involved here:

> If you draw a horizontal line at a given value for SIN X then it will pick out an infinite number of angles on the X-axis which all have the same value for SIN X.

Example 1: *"Find 6 different angles X such that Sin X = 0.94"*

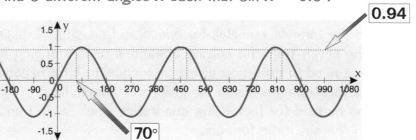

Method

1) SKETCH the extended SIN X graph.

2) Put a HORIZONTAL LINE across at 0.94.

3) DRAW LINES DOWN to the X-axis wherever the horizontal CROSSES THE CURVE.

4) Use your CALCULATOR to find INV SIN 0.94, to get the first angle (70^0 in this case).

5) The SYMMETRY is surely obvious. You can see that 70^0 is 20^0 away from the peak, so all the other angles are clearly 20^0 either side of the peaks at 90^0, 450^0, etc.

> Hence we can say that the SIN X = +0.94 for all the following angles:
> ..... -290^0, -250^0, 70^0, 110^0, 430^0, 470^0, 790^0, 830^0....

Example 2: *"Find three other angles which have the same Cosine as 65^0."*

ANSWER: 1) Use the calculator to find COS 65^0 = +0.423.
2) Draw the extended COS curve and a horizontal line across at + 0.423.
3) Draw the vertical lines from the intersections and use symmetry.

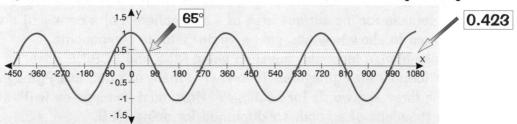

Since 65^0 is 25^0 below 90^0 the other angles shown must be: -425^0, -295^0, -65^0, etc.

The Acid Test: LEARN the FIVE graphs and the 3-point method above. Then turn over and write it all down.

1) Find the first 4 positive values and first two negative values for X such that
   a) SIN X = 0.5   b) COS X = -0.67   c) TAN X = 1

Revision Summary for Module Five

Here we are again — more great questions to test yourself with. Keep practising these questions *over and over again* until you can answer them *all*. Seriously, it's the best revision you can do.

Keep learning these basic facts until you know them

1) List the first ten triangle numbers?
2) Write down the 2 formulas for finding the nth term of a number pattern.
3) What does "D.O.T.S." stand for? Give two examples of it.
4) What is the method for multiplying out double brackets and squared brackets?
5) What are the rules for multiplying, dividing, adding and subtracting algebraic fractions?
6) Write down the formula triangles for speed and density. Explain how you use them.
7) What are the seven steps for solving equations or rearranging formulas?
8) What do you need to do if you divide an inequality by a negative number?
9) What is the three-stage method for graphical inequalities?
10) What is the method for factorising quadratics when "a" is 1 and when "a" isn't 1?
11) Write down the quadratic formula.
12) What are the four main steps for turning a quadratic into a completed square?
13) Write down the six steps for easy and seven steps for tricky simultaneous equations.
14) Write down the four steps of the trial and improvement method.
15) What are the three types of straight lines you should just know?
16) What do "m" and "c" in $y = mx + c$ represent?
17) How are the gradients of perpendicular lines related?
18) List the four main types of curve you might have to find an equation for.
19) Illustrate each of the four different types of graph transformation.
20) Describe the different features of a distance-time graph and a velocity-time graph.
21) Write down the three steps needed to find the area of a segment.
22) Write down the volume formula for a) a sphere   b) a prism   c) a cone   d) a pyramid.
23) What are the nine simple rules for circle geometry?
24) What is a locus? Describe, with diagrams, the four you should know.
25) Demonstrate how to draw accurate 60^0 and 90^0 angles.
26) What does TERRY stand for?
27) What details must be specified for each transformation?
28) What do "congruent" and "similar" mean? How do you tell if 2 triangles are congruent?
29) What three types of scale factor are there and what is the result of each?
30) How can you tell if a formula is a length, area or volume just by looking at it?
31) What is the formula for the surface area of a) a sphere   b) a cone   c) a cylinder?
32) Draw a diagram to show how you split a vector into its components.
33) Do the "Queen Mary's tugboats" question using SINE and COSINE rules.
34) What is the formula for Pythagoras' theorem? Where can you use Pythagoras?
35) What are the three key words for bearings? How must bearings be written?
36) Write down the steps of a good, solid method for doing TRIG.
37) Draw a diagram to illustrate angles of elevation and depression.
38) What three steps allow you to find the angle between a line and a plane?
39) Write down the SINE and COSINE rules and draw a properly labelled diagram.
40) List the 4 different types of SINE/COSINE question and which rule you need for each.
41) Draw the graphs of SIN, COS and TAN over 0°-360° and then –1080° to 1080°.

Answers

MODULE ONE

P.1 MEAN, MEDIAN, MODE AND RANGE: First: –14, –12, –5, –5, 0, 1, 3, 6, 7, 8, 10, 14, 18, 23, 25 Mean = 5.27,

Median = 6, Mode = –5, Range = 39   P.2 PROBABILITY: 2) $\frac{4}{52} \times \frac{3}{51} \times \frac{1}{50} = \frac{1}{11050}$

P.4 PROBABILITY:

1) $\frac{2}{7} \times \frac{1}{6} \times \frac{5}{6} \times \frac{4}{5} = \frac{40}{1260} = \frac{2}{63}$

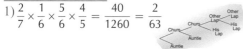

P.7 FREQUENCY TABLES:

No. of Phones	0	1	2	3	4	5	6	TOTALS
Frequency	1	25	53	34	22	5	1	141
No. × Frequency	0	25	106	102	88	25	6	352

Mean = 2.5, Median = 2,
Mode = 2, Range = 6

P.8 GROUPED FREQUENCY TABLES:

Length(cm)	15.5 —	16.5 —	17.5 —	18.5 – 19.5	TOTALS
Frequency	12	18	23	8	61
Mid-Interval Value	16	17	18	19	—
Freq × M I V	192	306	414	152	1064

1) Mean = 17.4
2) Modal Group = 17.5 — 18.5, Median ≈ 17.5

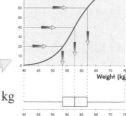

P.9 CUMULATIVE FREQUENCY:

Weight (kg)	41 – 45	46 – 50	51 – 55	56 – 60	61 – 65	66 – 70	71 – 75
Frequency	2	7	17	25	19	8	2
Cum. Freq.	2	9	26	51	70	78	80

Median = 58 kg, Lower Quartile = 53 kg,
Upper Quartile = 62 kg, Interquartile range = 9 kg

P.10 HISTOGRAMS AND FREQUENCY DENSITY: 1) 0–5: 10, 5–10: 30, 10–15: 40, 15–20: 50, 20–25: 35, 25–35: 20, 35–55: 20, 55–65: 40, 65–80: 180, 80–90: 140, 90–100: 20 2) 5

P.11 CORRELATION, DISPERSION AND SPREAD:

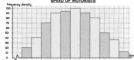  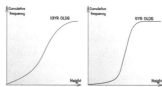

P.12 SAMPLING METHODS: 1) Sample too small, motorways not representative of average motorist, only done at one time of day and in one place, not easy to get accurate age from registration letter. Better approach: A more detailed survey which deals with all the above problems — surveying people emerging from various post offices with new tax discs might be good. Stratified sampling would be essential in choosing the post offices.

P.13 TIME SERIES: 1)a) period = 4 months b) Find the average of the readings from months 1– 4, then the average from months 2– 5, etc. (& you could plot these on a graph to see the trend.)

MODULE THREE

P.15 SQUARES,CUBES... 1)a) 81, 25, 36, 1, 64, 225 b) 8, 27, 125, 1, 64, 1000 2)a) 14.1 b) 3 c) –3
P.16 PRIME NUMBERS: 1) 2, 3, 5, 7, 11, 13, 17, 19, 23, 29, 31, 37, 41, 43, 47 2)a) 101, 103, 107, 109 b) none
c) 503, 509 P.17 MULTIPLES, FACTORS AND PRIME FACTORS: 1) 990 = 2 × 3 × 3 × 5 × 11
b) 160 = 2 × 2 × 2 × 2 × 2 × 5   P.18 LCM and HCF: 1) 7, 14, 21, 28, 35, 42, 49, 56, 63, 70; 9, 18, 27, 36, 45, 54, 63, 72, 81, 90; LCM = 63 2) 1, 2, 3, 4, 6, 9, 12, 18, 36; 1, 2, 3, 4, 6, 7, 12, 14, 21, 28, 42, 84; HCF = 12
P.19 POWERS AND ROOTS: 1)a) 3^8 b) 4 c) 8^{12} d) 1 e) 7^6 2)a) 64 b) 1/625 c) 1/5 d) 2 e) 125 f) 1/25 3)a) 1.53×10^{17}
b) 15.9 c) 2.89 P.20 MANIPULATING SURDS AND USE OF π: 1) $4\sqrt{2}$ 2) $1 + 2\sqrt{2}$
P.21 FRACTIONS AND DECIMALS: 1) 142857 / 999999 2) 7 / 200
P.22 DECIMALS AND RECIPROCALS: 1) 6614.4 2) 23.2 3)a) $\frac{1}{12}$ b) 4
P.24 STANDARD INDEX FORM: 1) 9.58×10^5; 1.8×10^{-4} 2) 4560 3)a) 2×10^{11} b) 2×10^{21}
P.25 BASIC ALGEBRA: 1)a) 12 b) –6 c) x 2)a) 18 b) –216 c) 2 d) –27 e) –336 3)a) 4x + y – 4 b) 2x + 8y – xy
P.26 FRACTIONS: 1)a) $\frac{3}{8}$ b) $\frac{27}{10} = 2\frac{7}{10}$ c) $\frac{11}{15}$ d) x = 13 e) y = 1 2)a) $\frac{8}{15}$ b) $\frac{8}{3} = 2\frac{2}{3}$ c) $\frac{7}{24}$ d) $\frac{3}{7}$ e) $\frac{3}{4}$
f) $\frac{112}{15} = 7\frac{7}{15}$ g) $2\frac{4}{11}$
P.27 PERCENTAGES: 1) 40% 2) 20,500 3) 1.39%   P.28 COMPOUND GROWTH AND DECAY: 1) 48 stick insects
2) 0.15m/s. Forever.   P.30 RATIOS: 1)a) 5:7 b) 2:3 c) 3:5 2) 17.5 bowls 3) £3500, £2100, £2800
P.32 CALCULATOR BUTTONS: 2)a) 6 x^y 8 = b) 6 EXP 8
c) 50 x^y ((–) 4 a^b/c 5) = or 50 x^y (–) 0.8 =
3) (23.3 + 35.8) ÷ (36 × 26.5) = 4)a) 4hrs 34 mins (12 secs) b) 5.5397 hrs
P.33 CONVERSION FACTORS: 1) 2,300m 2) £174 3) 3.2cm
P.34 METRIC AND IMPERIAL UNITS: 1) 15.75 litres 2) 200 or 220 yards 3) 115cm 4) 62.9p per litre 5) 104 km/h
P.36 ROUNDED OFF VALUES: 1) (4.22472 – 4.1556) ÷ 4.22472 = 0.01637 = 1.64%

Answers

P.37 PROPORTION: 1) Work out one 2) £8.05 3) 3 hrs   P.39 VARIATION: 1)a) 0.632 Hz b) 40.8cm

P.40 TYPICAL GRAPH QUESTIONS: 1)

x	-2	-1	0	1	2	3	4	5	6
y	15	8	3	0	-1	0	3	8	15

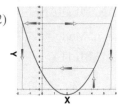

3) y = 3.8, x = –1.6 or 5.6

P.41 PLOTTING STRAIGHT LINE GRAPHS: 1)

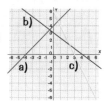

P.42 SOLVING EQUATIONS USING GRAPHS: 1) t = 0.7 or 4.3 2)a) x = -2.4, 0.4 b) x = –3, 1

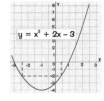

P.43 SIMULTANEOUS EQUATIONS AND GRAPHS:

1)a) x = 2, y = 4 b) x = 1½, y = 3 2) Solutions are: x = –2 or x = 1.5

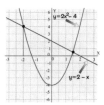

MODULE FIVE

P.45 NUMBER PATTERNS: 1) 162,486 2) 18, 29 3) 23, 30 4) 16, 8

P.46 FINDING THE NTH TERM: 1)a) 3n + 1 b) 5n–2 c) ½n(n + 1) d) n² – 2n + 4

P.48 MORE ALGEBRA: 1)a) (X – 4Y)(X + 4Y) b) (7 – 9PQ)(7 + 9PQ) 2) 6p²q – 8pq³ 3) 8g² + 16g – 10

4) 7xy² (2xy + 3 – 5x²y²) 5) c⁴/6d³ 6) $\frac{2(17g-6)}{5(3g-4)}$

P.49 SPEED AND DENSITY FORMULAS: 1) 1 hr 37 mins 30 secs 2) 16.5 g/cm³ 3) 603 g

P.50 SOLVING EQUATIONS: 1)a) x = 2 b) x = –0.2 or –1/5 c) x = $\sqrt{6}$

P.51 REARRANGING FORMULAS: 1) C = 5(F – 32)/9 2)a) p = –4y/3 b) p = rq/(r + q) c) p = $\pm\sqrt{rq/(r+q)}$

P.52 INEQUALITIES: 1) x ≥ –2 2)a) –6, –5, –4, –3, –2, –1, 0, 1, 2, 3, 4, 5, 6 b)–4, –3, –2, –1, 0, 1, 2, 3, 4

P.53 GRAPHICAL INEQUALITIES:

P.55 FACTORISING QUADRATICS: 1)a) x = 3 or–8
b) x = 7 or–1 c) x = 1 or –7 d) x = 4 or –3/5

P.56 THE QUADRATIC FORMULA: 1)a) x = 0.39 or –10.39
b) x = 1.46 or –0.46 c) x = 0.44 or –3.44

P.57 COMPLETING THE SQUARE: 2)a) x = 0.39 or –10.39
b) x = 1.46 or –0.46

P.58 SIMULTANEOUS EQUATIONS: 2) F = 3, G = –1

P.59 SIMULTANEOUS EQUATIONS: a) f = 4 & g = 0 OR f = 40 & g = 6 b) f = –5/3 & g = –2/3 OR f = 72 & g = 5
c) f = 9 & g = –3/2 OR f = 1 & g = 1/2 d) f = –3 & g = 33 OR f = 1/4 & g = –11/4

P.60 TRIAL AND IMPROVEMENT: 1) x = 2.4

P.61 FIVE GRAPHS YOU SHOULD RECOGNISE:

1)a) x² bucket shape b) –x³ wiggle (top left to bottom right)
c) +ve inverse proportion graph d) Straight line (–ve gradient)
e) –ve inverse proportion graph f) +x³ wiggle (bottom left to top right)
g) –x² upside down bucket h) Kˣ curve upwards through (0,1)

P.63 STRAIGHT LINE GRAPHS: "Y=mx + c"

1)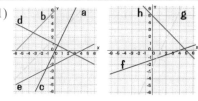

P.64 GRADIENTS AND GRAPHS OF CIRCLES: 1)a)–1/4 b) –2 c) 1/2 2)a) $\sqrt{1}$ b) 7 c) $\sqrt{20}$

P.65 FINDING EQUATIONS FROM GRAPHS: 1) P = 50, Q = 1.41

P.67 GRAPHS:SHIFTS AND STRETCHES:

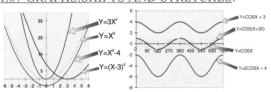

P.68 D/T AND V/T GRAPHS: 1) 0.5 km/h
2) Accel. 6m/s², 2m/s², –8m/s² (deceleration), speeds: 30m/s 50m/s.
P.69 AREA: 1) Perimeter 27.5 cm, Area 35.0 cm²
P.70 VOLUMES: 1)a) Trapezoidal Prism, V = 148.5 cm³
b) Cylinder, V=0.70 m³ c) Cone, 20.3m³ 2)33.5cm³, 179.6 cm³
P.71 LENGTH, AREA AND VOLUME:
1)a) Area b)Volume c) Length   2)   3) 364 cm²

Answers

<u>P.73 CIRCLE GEOMETRY:</u> 1) BCD = 90°, CBD = 42°, OBE = 48°, BEO = 48°, BOE = 84°, OEF = 90°, AEB = 42°

<u>P.76 THE FOUR TRANSFORMATIONS:</u> A → B, rotation of 90⁰ clockwise about the origin. E → A, enlargement, scale factor 2, centre (0, 0). F → B, enlargement, scale factor –2, centre (0, 0). B → C, reflection in the line Y = X. C → A, reflection in the Y-axis. A → D, translation of $\begin{pmatrix} -9 \\ -7 \end{pmatrix}$. A → E, enlargement, scale factor ½, centre (0, 0). B → F, enlargement, scale factor –½, centre (0, 0).

<u>P.78 SIMILARITY AND ENLARGEMENTS:</u> 1) A'(–3,–1.5), B'(–7.5,–3), C'(–6,–6) 2) 64 m²

<u>P.79 VECTORS:</u> a) $-\underset{\sim}{m} - \underset{\sim}{b}$ b) ½$\underset{\sim}{b}$ – ½$\underset{\sim}{a}$ + $\underset{\sim}{m}$ $(= \frac{1}{2}\overrightarrow{AC})$ c) ½$(\underset{\sim}{a} - \underset{\sim}{b})$ + $\underset{\sim}{m}$ d) ½$(\underset{\sim}{b} - \underset{\sim}{a})$

<u>P.80 "REAL LIFE" VECTOR QUESTIONS:</u>

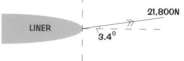

<u>P.81 PYTHAGORAS' THEOREM AND BEARINGS:</u> 1) BC = 8 m 2) 298° 3) 118°

<u>P.82 PYTHAGORAS, LINES AND LINE SEGMENTS:</u> 1) 5 units 2) A line continues to infinity, a line segment doesn't.

<u>P.84 TRIGONOMETRY — SIN, COS, TAN:</u> 1) x = 26.5 m 2) 23.6° 3) 32.6° (both)

<u>P.85 PYTHAGORAS AND TRIGONOMETRY IN 3D:</u> 1) 25.1° 2) $\sqrt{50}$

<u>P.87 THE SINE AND COSINE RULES:</u>
2) 17.13m, 68.8°, 41.2°

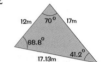

<u>P.89 ANGLES OF ANY SIZE:</u>
1) a) x = –330⁰, –210⁰, 30⁰, 150⁰, 390⁰, 510⁰
   b) x = –228⁰,–132⁰,132⁰, 228⁰, 492⁰, 588⁰
   c) –315⁰, –135⁰, 45⁰, 225⁰, 405⁰, 585⁰

Index

Index

MAHR41